Kaleidoscope

POEMS BY AMERICAN NEGRO POETS

Kaleidoscope

POEMS BY AMERICAN NEGRO POETS

EDITED AND WITH AN INTRODUCTION BY

Robert Hayden

HARCOURT, BRACE & WORLD, INC.
New York

036061

(CRB)

Curriculum-Related Books, selected and edited by the School Department of Harcourt, Brace & World, are titles of general interest for individual reading.

⊂B ACKNOWLEDGMENTS

FOR PERMISSION to reprint copyrighted material, grateful acknowledgment is made to the following authors, agents, and publishers:

SAMUEL W. ALLEN: "To Satch" and "A Moment Please" by Samuel W. Allen from *American Negro Poetry*, edited by Arna Bontemps.
BALLANTINE BOOKS, INC.: "Late Corner" and "Two Somewhat Different Epigrams" by Langston Hughes, © 1957 by Ballantine Books, Inc., and "Where? When? Which?" by Langston Hughes, © 1956 by The Colorado Review, from *New Poems by American Poets 1 2*, edited by Rolfe Humphries, 1957.
GERALD WILLIAM BARRAX: "The Sacrifice," "Patroness," "Black Narcissus," "Christmas 1959 et cetera," and "The Death of a Squirrel in McKinley Park" by Gerald William Barrax.
ARNA BONTEMPS: "Close Your Eyes," "Southern Mansion," "Reconnaissance," and "A Black Man Talks of Reaping" from *American Negro Poetry*, edited by Arna Bontemps, copyright © 1963 by Arna Bontemps. "To a Young Girl Leaving the Hill Country" from *Personals* by Arna Bontemps, copyright © 1964 by Arna Bontemps.

iv

⊂⊃ PICTURE CREDITS

To Paul Breman

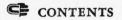 CONTENTS

THE QUESTION whether we can speak with any real justification of "Negro poetry" arises often today. Some object to the term because it has been used disparagingly to indicate a kind of pseudo-poetry concerned with the race problem to the exclusion of almost everything else. Others hold that Negro poetry *per se* could only be produced in black Africa. Seen from this point of view, the poetry of the American Negro, its "specialized" content notwithstanding, is obviously not to be thought of as existing apart from the rest of our literature, but as having been shaped over some three centuries by social, moral, and literary forces essentially American.

Those who presently avow themselves "poets of the Negro revolution" argue that they do indeed constitute a separate group or school, since the purpose of their writing is to give Negroes a sense of human dignity and provide them with ideological weapons. A belligerent race pride moves these celebrants of Black Power to declare themselves not simply "poets," but "Negro poets." However, Countee Cullen, the brilliant lyricist of the Harlem Renaissance in the 1920's, insisted that he be considered a "poet," not a "Negro poet," for he did not want to be restricted to racial themes nor have his poetry judged solely on the basis of its relevance to the Negro struggle.

Cullen was aware of a peculiar risk Negro poets

have had to face. The tendency of American critics has been to label the established Negro writer a "spokesman for his race." There are, as we have seen, poets who think of themselves in that role. But the effect of such labeling is to place any Negro author in a kind of literary ghetto where the standards applied to other writers are not likely to be applied to him, since he, being a "spokesman for his race," is not considered primarily a writer but a species of race-relations man, the leader of a cause, the voice of protest.

Protest has been a recurring element in the writing of American Negroes, a fact hardly to be wondered at, given the social conditions under which they have been forced to live. And the Negro poet's devotion to the cause of freedom is not in any way reprehensible, for throughout history poets have often been champions of human liberty. But bad poetry is another matter, and there is no denying that a great deal of "race poetry" is poor, because its content seems ready-made and art is displaced by argument.

Phillis Wheatley (c. 1750–1784), the first poet of African descent to win some measure of recognition, had almost nothing to say about the plight of her people. And if she resented her own ambiguous position in society, she did not express her resentment. One reason for her silence is that, although brought to Boston as a slave, she never lived as one. Another is that as a neoclassical poet she would scarcely have thought it proper to reveal much of herself in her poetry, although we do get brief glimpses of her in the poem addressed to the Earl of Dartmouth and in "On Being Brought from Africa to America." Neoclassicism emphasized reason rather than emotion and favored elegance and formality. The English poet, Alexander Pope, was the acknowledged master of this style, and in submitting to his influence Phillis Wheatley produced poetry that was as good as that of her American contemporaries. She actually wrote better than some of them.

But the poetry of Phillis Wheatley and her fellow poet, Jupiter Hammon, has historical and not literary interest for us now. The same can be said of much of eighteenth-century American poetry in general. Not until the nineteenth century did the United States begin to have literature of unqualified merit and originality. There were no Negro poets of stature in the period before the Civil War, but there were several with talent, among them George Moses Horton (1797–c. 1883) and Frances E. W. Harper (1825–1911). Didactic and sentimental, they wrote with competence and moral fervor in the manner of their times. Their poetry is remembered chiefly because it contributed to the antislavery struggle, and because it testifies to the creative efforts of Negroes under disheartening conditions.

During the Reconstruction era, writers of "local color" turned for material to the history, the customs, and the dialect that made each section of the country different from the others. James Whitcomb Riley published poems in the Hoosier dialect of Indiana. White southern authors wrote nostalgically of The Old South and through their idealization of ante-bellum plantation life created the "plantation tradition" in literature. Thomas Nelson Page, for example, wrote Negro dialect verse that was an apology for slavery, picturing the Negro as docile and happy in servitude. Both Riley and Page had some influence on Paul Laurence Dunbar (1872–1906), the most important Negro poet to emerge in the latter part of the century. Some of Dunbar's dialect verse is in the plantation tradition, but it is essentially different from the kind written by the southern apologists, his portrayals of Negro life being more sympathetic and more authentic. Dunbar became famous for his work in this medium, and other Negro poets imitated him. But he himself put less value on his dialect verse than he did on his poems in standard English.

In the twentieth century Negro poets have abandoned dialect for an idiom truer to folk speech. The change has been due not only to differences in social outlook on their part but also to revolutionary developments in American poetry. The New Poetry movement, which began before the First World War and reached its definitive point in the 1920's, represented a break with the past. Free verse, diction close to everyday speech, a realistic approach to life, and the use of material once considered unpoetic— these were the goals of the movement. The Negro poet-critic, William Stanley Braithwaite, encouraged the "new" poetry through his articles in the *Boston Evening Transcript* and his yearly anthologies of magazine verse.

The New Negro movement or Negro Renaissance, resulting from the social, political, and artistic awakening of Negroes in the twenties, brought into prominence poets whose work showed the influence of the poetic revolution. Protest became more defiant, racial bitterness and racial pride more outspoken than ever before. Negro history and folklore were explored as new sources of inspiration. Spirituals, blues, and jazz suggested themes and verse patterns to young poets like Jean Toomer and Langston Hughes. Certain conventions, notably what has been called "literary Garveyism," grew out of a fervent Negro nationalism. Marcus Garvey, leader of the United Negro Improvement Association, advocated a "return" to Africa, the lost homeland, and nearly all the Renaissance poets wrote poems about their spiritual ties to Africa, about the dormant fires of African paganism in the Negro soul that the white man's civilization could never extinguish. Countee Cullen's "Heritage" is one of the best of these poems, even though the Africa it presents is artificial, romanticized, and it reiterates exotic clichés in vogue during the period when it was written.

Harlem was the center of the Negro Renaissance, which for that reason is also referred to as the Harlem Renaissance. Two magazines, *The Crisis* and *Opportunity*, gave aid and encouragement to Negro writers by publishing their work and by awarding literary prizes.

In the decades since the New Negro movement, which ended with the twenties, protest and race consciousness have continued to find expression in the poetry of the American Negro. But other motivating forces are also in evidence. There are Negro poets who believe that any poet's most clearly defined task is to create with honesty and sincerity poems that will illuminate human experience —not exclusively "Negro experience." They reject the idea of poetry as racial propaganda, of poetry that functions as a kind of sociology. Their attitude is not wholly new, of course, being substantially that of Dunbar and Cullen. In counterpoise to it is the "Beat" or "nonacademic" view held by poets who are not only in rebellion against middle-class ideals and the older poetic traditions but who also advocate a militant racism in a definitely "Negro" poetry.

It has come to be expected of Negro poets that they will address themselves to the race question—and that they will all say nearly the same things about it. Such "group unity" is more apparent than real. Differences in vision and emphasis, fundamental differences in approach to the art of poetry itself, modify and give diversity to the writing of these poets, even when they employ similar themes. And certainly there is no agreement among them as to what the much debated role of the Negro poet should be.

This anthology is not intended as a comprehensive survey, but, rather, as a guide that will help students gain some notion of the salient features of a particular area of the American literary landscape. Not all the selections will be read with the same degree of interest, but it is hoped that the majority of them will afford enjoyment and deepen the appreciation of poetry.

Perhaps it would not be amiss to say in conclusion that neither the editor nor his publisher should be understood as necessarily endorsing the long-established custom of segregating the work of Negro poets within the covers of a separate anthology. Yet where, except in a collection such as the present one, is the student to gather any impression of the nature and scope of the Negro's contribution to American poetry?

Kaleidoscope

POEMS BY AMERICAN NEGRO POETS

PHILLIS WHEATLEY
was brought as a child from Senegal to Boston, where she was purchased by John Wheatley, a well-to-do tailor, as a gift for his wife. The little girl's precocity encouraged the Wheatleys to begin educating her, and within a short time she was able to read the Bible. She learned Latin and read both classical and modern literature, her favorite English poet being Alexander Pope. She delighted the Wheatleys and their friends by writing poems herself, most of them elegies in the neoclassic manner. Her first poem was published in 1770, when she was about seventeen, and it was entitled "A Poem by Phillis, A Negro Girl in Boston, on the Death of the Reverend George Whitefield." It brought her to the attention of the Countess of Huntingdon, the minister's patroness.

Although Phillis had been a slave in name only, the Wheatleys formally manumitted her in 1773. Concern for her health at this time prompted them to send her to London with their son Nathaniel in the hope that the ocean air and a change of climate would be good for her. In London "The Sable Muse," as she has been called, was lionized by the Countess of Huntingdon and her circle. Indeed, preparations were under way for her presentation at the royal court when she received word that Mrs. Wheatley was ill and left for Boston with Nathaniel. The Countess had arranged previously for the publication of Phillis's poetry, and *Poems on Various Subjects, Religious and Moral* —the only collection of her work ever published—appeared in London later that year. It remained popular for a long time, appearing in various editions during the eighteenth and nineteenth centuries. The definitive edition, which includes the poet's letters, was issued in 1966.

Phillis's life changed radically after she left the Wheatley household. Her marriage to John Peters, a free Negro, was unfortunate. She lived in poverty, her three children died in infancy, and her health, always delicate, grew steadily worse. She seems to have been too proud to let the surviving members of the Wheatley family know of her condition or to ask them for help. She died in Boston in 1784.

Phillis Wheatley's poetry has been derided by some critics as "mockingbird" verse, but recent scholarship reveals that she was not a mere imitator but an intellectual poet who consciously used the devices of neoclassicism because they suited her purpose.

From TO THE RIGHT HONORABLE WILLIAM, EARL OF
DARTMOUTH, HIS MAJESTY'S PRINCIPAL SECRETARY OF
STATE FOR NORTH AMERICA, ETC.

   . . .

    Should you, my lord, while you pursue my song
Wonder from whence my love of *Freedom* sprung,
Whence flow these wishes for the common good,
By feeling hearts alone best understood,
I, young in life, by seeming cruel fate
Was snatch'd from *Afric's* fancy'd happy seat:
What pangs excruciating must molest,
What sorrows labour in my parent's breast?
Steel'd was the soul and by no misery mov'd
That from a father seiz'd his babe belov'd
Such, such my case. And can I then but pray
Others may never feel tyrannic sway?

   . . .

Celestial choir, enthron'd in realms of light,
Columbia's scenes of glorious toils I write.
While freedom's cause her anxious breast alarms,
She flashes dreadful in refulgent arms.
See mother earth her offspring's fate bemoan,
And nations gaze at scenes before unknown;
See the bright beams of heaven's revolving light
Involved in sorrows and the veil of night!

The goddess comes, she moves divinely fair,
Olive and laurel binds her golden hair:
Wherever shines this native of the skies,
Unnumber'd charms and recent graces rise.

Muse! bow propitious while my pen relates
How pour her armies through a thousand gates,
As when Eolus heaven's fair face deforms,
Enwrapp'd in tempest and a night of storms;
Astonish'd ocean feels the wild uproar,
The refluent surges beat the sounding shore;
Or thick as leaves in Autumn's golden reign,
Such, and so many, moves the warrior's train.
In bright array they seek the work of war,
Where high unfurl'd the ensign waves in air.
Shall I to Washington their praise recite?

Enough thou know'st them in the fields of fight.
Thee, first in peace and honours,—we demand
The grace and glory of thy martial band.
Fam'd for thy valour, for thy virtues more,
Hear every tongue thy guardian aid implore!

One century scarce perform'd its destined round,
When Gallic powers Columbia's fury found;
And so may you, whoever dares disgrace
The land of freedom's heaven-defended race!
Fix'd are the eyes of nations on the scales,
For in their hopes Columbia's arm prevails.
Anon Britannia droops the pensive head,
While round increase the rising hills of dead.
Ah! cruel blindness to Columbia's state!
Lament thy thirst of boundless power too late.

Proceed, great chief, with virtue on thy side,
Thy ev'ry action let the goddess guide.
A crown, a mansion, and a throne that shine,
With gold unfading, Washington! be thine.

'Twas mercy brought me from my *Pagan* land,
Taught my benighted soul to understand
That there's a God, that there's a *Saviour* too;
Once I redemption neither sought nor knew.
Some view our sable race with scornful eye,
"Their color is a diabolic die."
Remember, *Christians, Negroes,* black as *Cain,*
May be refined, and join th' angelic train.

GEORGE MOSES HORTON,
a slave belonging to the Hortons of Northampton County,
North Carolina, learned to read and write while hired out
to the president of the University of North Carolina. He
began to write verse at this time, and students paid him to
compose love-poems for them. Horton's first volume, *The
Hope of Liberty*, published in Raleigh in 1829, represented
in quite literal fashion his attempt to write his way out of
slavery, for he hoped that the sale of the book would bring
him enough money to buy his freedom. But Horton remained a slave until he fled to the Union Army in 1865.
Naked Genius, another collection of verse, came out the
same year. He is said to have spent the rest of his life in
Philadelphia, dying there probably in 1883, but not much
is known of him after his escape from slavery.

Horton's poems are imitative and sentimental. They
hold historical rather than literary value for us today. But
they show talent, and they clearly refute the notion of the
contented slave.

I feel myself in need
    Of the inspiring strains of ancient lore,
My heart to lift, my empty mind to feed,
    And all the world explore.

I know that I am old
    And never can recover what is past,
But for the future may some light unfold
    And soar from ages blast.

I feel resolved to try,
    My wish to prove, my calling to pursue,
Or mount up from the earth into the sky,
    To show what Heaven can do:

My genius from a boy,
    Has fluttered like a bird within my heart;
But could not thus confined her powers employ,
    Impatient to depart.

She like a restless bird,
    Would spread her wings, her power to be unfurl'd,
And let her songs be loudly heard,
    And dart from world to world.

9

Alas! and am I born for this,
    To wear this slavish chain?
Deprived of all created bliss,
    Through hardship, toil and pain!

How long have I in bondage lain,
    And languished to be free!
Alas! and must I still complain—
    Deprived of liberty.

Oh, Heaven! and is there no relief
    This side the silent grave—
To soothe the pain—to quell the grief
    And anguish of a slave?

Come Liberty, thou cheerful sound,
    Roll through my ravished ears!
Come, let my grief in joys be drowned,
    And drive away my fears.

Say unto foul oppression, Cease:
    Ye tyrants rage no more,
And let the joyful trump of peace,
    Now bid the vassal soar.

Soar on the pinions of that dove
    Which long has cooed for thee,
And breathed her notes from Afric's grove,
    The sound of Liberty.

Oh, Liberty! thou golden prize,
    So often sought by blood—
We crave thy sacred sun to rise,
    The gift of nature's God!

Bid Slavery hide her haggard face,
    And barbarism fly:
I scorn to see the sad disgrace
    In which enslaved I lie.

Dear Liberty! upon thy breast,
    I languish to respire;
And like the Swan unto her nest,
    I'd to thy smiles retire.

Oh, blest asylum—heavenly balm!
    Unto thy boughs I flee—
And in thy shades the storm shall calm,
    With songs of Liberty!

FRANCES ELLEN WATKINS HARPER, born in Baltimore in 1825, was a lecturer for the Anti-Slavery Society of Maine, an Underground Railroad agent, a temperance worker, and a leader in religious and women's organizations as well as one of the most popular poets of her day. One marvels that she ever found time to write. *Poems on Various Subjects,* which was published in 1854 and went through several editions, was followed by *Poems* in 1871. She also wrote fiction. Her books were enthusiastically received, and she was much in demand as a reader of her verse and as a public speaker. She died in 1911.

As a poet Mrs. Harper was most successful when dealing with the cause of Negro freedom, to which she dedicated her life.

The sale began—young girls were there,
    Defenceless in their wretchedness,
Whose stifled sobs of deep despair
    Revealed their anguish and distress.

And mothers stood with streaming eyes,
    And saw their dearest children sold;
Unheeded rose their bitter cries,
    While tyrants bartered them for gold.

And woman, with her love and truth—
    For these in sable forms may dwell—
Gaz'd on the husband of her youth,
    With anguish none may paint or tell.

And men, whose sole crime was their hue,
    The impress of their Maker's hand,
And frail and shrinking children, too,
    Were gathered in that mournful band.

Ye who have laid your love to rest,
    And wept above their lifeless clay,
Know not the anguish of that breast,
    Whose lov'd are rudely torn away.

Ye may not know how desolate
    Are bosoms rudely forced to part,
And how a dull and heavy weight
    Will press the life-drops from the heart.

PAUL LAURENCE DUNBAR, during his lifetime, was one of America's most popular poets. Dunbar was born in Dayton, Ohio, in 1872 and educated in the public schools there. While employed as an elevator boy in a Dayton hotel, he brought out a book of poems at his own expense, *Oak and Ivy* (1893). It was followed in 1895 by *Majors and Minors,* also privately printed, which attracted the interest of William Dean Howells, the most influential literary critic of the period. Howells's enthusiasm, especially for the dialect pieces in the volume, led to the publication of Dunbar's third book, *Lyrics of Lowly Life,* in 1896, which included the best from the first two collections.

The critic's commendatory preface won recognition for the young poet, but it also had something of a negative effect. Howells, though commenting favorably on the poems in standard English, emphasized the artistry shown by the dialect poems, in which, he said, Dunbar had felt Negro life "aesthetically" and expressed it "lyrically." Such critical approval helped to popularize Dunbar as chiefly a dialect poet. And Dunbar was to write later: "But ah, the world, it turned to praise / A jingle in a broken tongue."

His dialect poems are still more familiar today than his others, though they have less appeal for us now. Given the limitations of the plantation genre itself, they are frequently of high quality. Dunbar idealized the life of "the lowly" and sentimentalized it, but he did not burlesque it. He laughed with his people, not at them, portraying them with affection in verse markedly rhythmic and musical. Yet he did not entirely avoid the stereotypes of the Negro demanded by his times; if he had, he would have been less popular than he was. He enjoyed phenomenal success as a black poet who wrote with charm and humor of his own race, though he would have preferred unqualified acceptance as a lyric poet.

His poems in "literary" English show technical skill and variety of form. Predominantly lyrical, they are most appealing when most personal. Many of them, however, echo the tired romanticism characteristic of the poetry of his era. Protest is not a significant element in his work, but it is implicit in "The Haunted Oak" and in "Robert Gould Shaw," both reprinted here.

Dunbar died in 1906 at the age of thirty-four. Poor health and great unhappiness in spite of his achievements had overshadowed his last years. In his brief career he produced four novels, four collections of short stories, librettos for musicals, and, in addition to the volumes already mentioned, the following books of poems: *Lyrics of the Hearthside* (1899), *Lyrics of Love and Laughter* (1903), and *Lyrics of Sunshine and Shadow* (1905).

I am the mother of sorrows,
    I am the ender of grief;
I am the bud and the blossom,
    I am the late-falling leaf.

I am thy priest and thy poet,
    I am thy serf and thy king;
I cure the tears of the heartsick,
    When I come near they shall sing.

White are my hands as the snow-drop;
    Swart are my fingers as clay;
Dark is my frown as the midnight,
    Fair is my brow as the day.

Battle and war are my minions,
    Doing my will as divine;
I am the calmer of passions,
    Peace is a nursling of mine.

Speak to me gently or curse me,
    Seek me or fly from my sight;
I am thy fool in the morning,
    Thou art my slave in the night.

Down to the grave will I take thee,
  Out from the noise of the strife;
Then shalt thou see me and know me—
  Death, then, no longer, but life.

Then shalt thou sing at my coming,
  Kiss me with passionate breath,
Clasp me and smile to have thought me
  Aught save the foeman of Death.

Come to me, brother, when weary,
  Come when thy lonely heart swells;
I'll guide thy footsteps and lead thee
  Down where the Dream Woman dwells.

She told the story, and the whole world wept
    At wrongs and cruelties it had not known
    But for this fearless woman's voice alone.
    She spoke to consciences that long had slept:
Her message, Freedom's clear reveille, swept
    From heedless hovel to complacent throne.
    Command and prophecy were in the tone
    And from its sheath the sword of justice leapt.
Around two peoples swelled a fiery wave,
    But both came forth transfigured from the flame.
Blest be the hand that dared be strong to save,
    And blest be she who in our weakness came—
    Prophet and priestess! At one stroke she gave
    A race to freedom and herself to fame.

* Harriet Beecher Stowe (1811–1896) was the author of the famous antislavery novel, *Uncle Tom's Cabin*.

Dear critic, who my lightness so deplores,
Would I might study to be prince of bores,
Right wisely would I rule that dull estate—
But, sir, I may not, till you abdicate.

He sang of life, serenely sweet,
    With, now and then, a deeper note.
    From some high peak, nigh yet remote,
He voiced the world's absorbing beat.

He sang of love when earth was young,
    And Love, itself, was in his lays.
    But ah, the world, it turned to praise
A jingle in a broken tongue.

Pray why are you so bare, so bare,
    Oh, bough of the old oak-tree;
And why, when I go through the shade you throw,
    Runs a shudder over me?

My leaves were green as the best, I trow,
    And sap ran free in my veins,
But I saw in the moonlight dim and weird
    A guiltless victim's pains.

I bent me down to hear his sigh;
    I shook with his gurgling moan,
And I trembled sore when they rode away,
    And left him here alone.

They'd charged him with the old, old crime,
    And set him fast in jail:
Oh, why does the dog howl all night long,
    And why does the night wind wail?

He prayed his prayer and he swore his oath,
    And he raised his hand to the sky;
But the beat of hoofs smote on his ear,
    And the steady tread drew nigh.

21

Who is it rides by night, by night,
    Over the moonlit road?
And what is the spur that keeps the pace,
    What is the galling goad?

And now they beat at the prison door,
    "Ho, keeper, do not stay!
We are friends of him whom you hold within,
    And we fain would take him away

"From those who ride fast on our heels
    With mind to do him wrong;
They have no care for his innocence,
    And the rope they bear is long."

They have fooled the jailer with lying words,
    They have fooled the man with lies;
The bolts unbar, the locks are drawn,
    And the great door open flies.

Now they have taken him from the jail,
    And hard and fast they ride,
And the leader laughs low down in his throat,
    As they halt my trunk beside.

Oh, the judge, he wore a mask of black,
    And the doctor one of white,
And the minister, with his oldest son,
    Was curiously bedight.

Oh, foolish man, why weep you now?
    'Tis but a little space,
And the time will come when these shall dread
    The mem'ry of your face.

I feel the rope against my bark,
  And the weight of him in my grain,
I feel in the throe of his final woe
  The touch of my own last pain.

And never more shall leaves come forth
  On a bough that bears the ban;
I am burned with dread, I am dried and dead,
  From the curse of a guiltless man.

And ever the judge rides by, rides by,
  And goes to hunt the deer,
And ever another rides his soul
  In the guise of a mortal fear.

And ever the man he rides me hard,
  And never a night stays he;
For I feel his curse as a haunted bough,
  On the trunk of a haunted tree.

This is the debt I pay
Just for one riotous day,
Years of regret and grief,
Sorrow without relief.

Pay it I will to the end—
Until the grave, my friend,
Gives me a true release—
Gives me the clasp of peace.

Slight was the thing I bought,
Small was the debt I thought,
Poor was the loan at best—
God! but the interest!

ROBERT GOULD SHAW*

Why was it that the thunder voice of Fate
    Should call thee, studious, from the classic groves,
    Where calm-eyed Pallas with still footstep roves,
And charge thee seek the turmoil of the state?
What bade thee hear the voice and rise elate,
    Leave home and kindred and thy spicy loaves,
    To lead th' unlettered and despised droves
To manhood's home and thunder at the gate?

Far better the slow blaze of Learning's light,
    The cool and quiet of her dearer fane,
Than this hot terror of a hopeless fight,
    This cold endurance of the final pain,—
Since thou and those who with thee died for right
    Have died, the Present teaches, but in vain!

* Colonel Robert Gould Shaw was in command of the Fifty-fourth
Massachusetts, a Negro regiment, at the battle of Fort Wagner (South
Carolina, July 18, 1863), in which he was killed.

JAMES WELDON JOHNSON
had an extremely varied life, won many honors and distinctions, and produced significant work in both poetry and prose. He was born in Jacksonville, Florida, in 1871 and became the first Negro after Reconstruction to be admitted to the bar in that state. He gave up law, however, to collaborate with his brother J. Rosamond Johnson on a series of musical comedies for the New York stage. He subsequently held diplomatic posts in Venezuela and Nicaragua. While in the consular service, he wrote the controversial novel, *The Autobiography of an Ex-Colored Man* (1912). He later became the first executive secretary of the NAACP. In 1925 he was given the Spingarn Medal for distinguished achievement. He was Professor of Creative Literature at Fisk University from 1930 until his death in an automobile accident in 1938.

Johnson's poetry includes dialect pieces in the manner of Dunbar, poems expressing racial pride and racial protest, and free verse adaptations of folk material, as well as personal lyrics and satire. His poetry is often conventional in structure and diction, and some of it is more effective as eloquent social statement than as poetry. But *God's Trombones: Seven Negro Sermons in Verse* (1927) and *St. Peter Relates an Incident of the Resurrection Day* (1930) show originality and boldness of design. Johnson's other books include *Fifty Years and Other Poems* (1922), *Along This Way* (1933), and *St. Peter Relates an Incident: Selected Poems* (1935).

Eternities—now numbering six or seven—
Hung heavy on the hands of all in heaven.
Archangels tall and fair had reached the stage
Where they began to show some signs of age.

The faces of the flaming seraphim
Were slightly drawn, their eyes were slightly dim.
The cherubs, too, for now—oh, an infinite while
Had worn but a wistful shade of their dimpling smile.

The serried singers of the celestial choir
Disclosed a woeful want of pristine fire;
When they essayed to strike the glad refrain,
Their attack was weak, their tone revealed voice strain.

Their expression seemed to say, "We must! We must!"
    though
'Twas more than evident they lacked the gusto;
It could not be elsewise—that fact all can agree on—
Chanting the selfsame choral æon after æon.

Thus was it that Saint Peter at the gate
Began a brand new thing in heaven: to relate
Some reminiscences from heavenly history,
Which had till then been more or less a mystery.

So now and then, by turning back the pages,
Were whiled away some moments from the ages,
Was gained a respite from the monotony
That can't help settling on eternity.

II

Now, there had been a lapse of ages hoary,
And the angels clamored for another story.
"Tell us a tale, Saint Peter," they entreated;
And gathered close around where he was seated.

Saint Peter stroked his beard,
And "Yes," he said
By the twinkle in his eye
And the nodding of his head.

A moment brief he fumbled with his keys—
It seemed to help him call up memories—
Straightway there flashed across his mind the one
About the unknown soldier
Who came from Washington.

The hosts stood listening,
Breathlessly awake;
And thus Saint Peter spake:

III

'Twas Resurrection morn,
And Gabriel blew a blast upon his horn
That echoed through the arches high and vast
Of Time and Space—a long resounding blast

To wake the dead, dead for a million years;
A blast to reach and pierce their dust-stopped ears;

To quicken them, wherever they might be,
Deep in the earth or deeper in the sea.

A shudder shook the world, and gaping graves
Gave up their dead. Out from the parted waves
Came the prisoners of old ocean. The dead belonging
To every land and clime came thronging.

From the four corners of all the earth they drew,
Their faces radiant and their bodies new.
Creation pulsed and swayed beneath the tread
Of all the living, and all the risen dead.

Swift-winged heralds of heaven flew back and forth,
Out of the east, to the south, the west, the north,
Giving out quick commands, and yet benign,
Marshaling the swarming milliards into line.

The recording angel in words of thundering might,
At which the timid, doubting souls took fright,
Bade all to await the grand roll-call; to wit,
To see if in the Book their names were writ.

The multitudinous business of the day
Progressed, but naturally, not without delay.
Meanwhile, within the great American border
There was the issuance of a special order.

IV

The word went forth, spoke by some grand panjandrum,
Perhaps, by some high potentate of Klandom,
That all the trusty patriotic mentors,
And duly qualified Hundred-Percenters

Should forthwith gather together upon the banks
Of the Potomac, there to form their ranks,
March to the tomb, by orders to be given,
And escort the unknown soldier up to heaven.

Compliantly they gathered from each region,
The G.A.R., the D.A.R., the Legion,
Veterans of wars—Mexican, Spanish, Haitian—
Trustees of the patriotism of the nation;

Key Men, Watchmen, shunning circumlocution,
The Sons of the This and That and of the Revolution;
Not to forget, there gathered every man
Of the Confederate Veterans and the Ku-Klux Klan.

The Grand Imperial Marshal gave the sign;
Column on column, the marchers fell in line;
Majestic as an army in review,
They swept up Washington's wide avenue.

Then, through the long line ran a sudden flurry,
The marchers in the rear began to hurry;
They feared unless the procession hastened on,
The unknown soldier might be risen and gone.

The fear was groundless; when they arrived, in fact,
They found the grave entirely intact.
(Resurrection plans were long, long past completing
Ere there was thought of re-enforced concreting.)

They heard a faint commotion in the tomb,
Like the stirring of a child within the womb;

At once they saw the plight, and set about
The job to dig the unknown soldier out.

They worked away, they labored with a will,
They toiled with pick, with crowbar, and with drill
To cleave a breach; nor did the soldier shirk;
Within his limits, he helped to push the work.

He, underneath the débris, heaved and hove
Up toward the opening which they cleaved and clove;
Through it, at last, his towering form loomed
        big and bigger—
"Great God Almighty! Look!" they cried,
        "he is a nigger!"

Surprise and consternation and dismay
Swept over the crowd; none knew just what to say
Or what to do. And all fell back aghast.
Silence—but only an instant did it last.

Bedlam: They clamored, they railed, some roared, some
        bleated;
All of them felt that somehow they'd been cheated.
The question rose: What to do with him, then?
The Klan was all for burying him again.

The scheme involved within the Klan's suggestion
Gave rise to a rather nice metaphysical question:
Could he be forced again through death's dark portal,
Since now his body and soul were both immortal?

Would he, forsooth, the curious-minded queried,
Even in concrete, re-entombed, stay buried?

In a moment more, midst the pile of broken stone,
The unknown soldier stood, and stood alone.

V

The day came to a close.
And heaven—hell too—was filled with them that rose.
I shut the pearly gate and turned the key;
For Time was now merged into Eternity.

I gave one last look over the jasper wall,
And afar descried a figure dark and tall:
The unknown soldier, dust-stained and begrimed,
Climbing his way to heaven, and singing as he climbed:
   Deep river, my home is over Jordan,
   Deep river, I want to cross over into camp-ground.

Climbing and singing—
   Deep river, my home is over Jordan,
   Deep river, I want to cross over into camp-ground.

Nearer and louder—
   Deep river, my home is over Jordan,
   Deep river, I want to cross over into camp-ground.

At the jasper wall—
   Deep river, my home is over Jordan,
   Deep river,
   Lord,
   I want to cross over into camp-ground.

I rushed to the gate and flung it wide,
Singing, he entered with a loose, long stride;
Singing and swinging up the golden street,

The music married to the tramping of his feet.
Tall, black soldier-angel marching alone,
Swinging up the golden street, saluting at the great white
      throne.
Singing, singing, singing, singing clear and strong.
Singing, singing, singing, till heaven took up the song:
    Deep river, my home is over Jordan,
    Deep river, I want to cross over into camp-ground.

VI

The tale was done,
The angelic hosts dispersed,
    but not till after
There ran through heaven
Something that quivered
    'twixt tears and laughter.

ANNE SPENCER,
born in Bramwell, West Virginia in 1882, was for many
years the librarian of Dunbar High School in Lynchburg,
Virginia. Although she has never published a book, her
poems have become known through inclusion in various
anthologies.

Mrs. Spencer's most engaging poems show dramatic
compression and sharpness of image and phrase, though
sometimes her diction is rather Victorian. Her style in general tends to be cryptic, philosophical. She is no pleader of
causes. She has obviously felt no compulsion to comment
on the race issue in the few poems she has been willing to
publish.

Gay little Girl-of-the-Diving-Tank,
I desire a name for you,
Nice, as a right glove fits;
For you—who amid the malodorous
Mechanics of this unlovely thing,
Are darling of spirit and form.
I know you—a glance, and what you are
Sits-by-the-fire in my heart.
My Limousine-Lady knows you, or
Why does the slant-envy of her eye mark
Your straight air and radiant inclusive smile?
Guilt pins a fig-leaf; Innocence is its own adorning.
The bull-necked man knows you—this first time
His itching flesh sees form divine and vibrant health
And thinks not of his avocation.
I came incuriously—
Set on no diversion save that my mind
Might safely nurse its brood of misdeeds
In the presence of a blind crowd.

The color of life was gray.
Everywhere the setting seemed right
For my mood.
Here the sausage and garlic booth
Sent unholy incense skyward;
There a quivering female-thing

Gestured assignations, and lied
To call it dancing;
There, too, were games of chance
With chances for none;
But oh! Girl-of-the-Tank, at last!
Gleaming Girl, how intimately pure and free
The gaze you send the crowd,
As though you know the dearth of beauty
In its sordid life.
We need you—my Limousine-Lady,
The bull-necked man and I.
Seeing you here brave and water-clean,
Leaven for the heavy ones of earth,
I am swift to feel that what makes
The plodder glad is good; and
Whatever is good is God.
The wonder is that you are here;
I have seen the queer in queer places,
But never before a heaven-fed
Naiad of the Carnival-Tank!
Little Diver, Destiny for you,
Like as for me, is shod in silence;
Years may seep into your soul
The bacilli of the usual and the expedient;
I implore Neptune to claim his child to-day!

Ah, how poets sing and die!
Make one song and Heaven takes it;
Have one heart and Beauty breaks it;
Chatterton, Shelley, Keats and I—
Ah, how poets sing and die!

GEORGIA DOUGLASS JOHNSON
studied music at the Oberlin Conservatory in Ohio, but
deciding not to become a professional musician, turned to
the writing of poetry. She won some recognition as a lyric
poet with *The Heart of a Woman* (1918), *Bronze* (1922),
and *An Autumn Love Cycle* (1928). Her last book, *Share
My World,* appeared in 1962. For many years, until her
death in 1965, Mrs. Johnson lived in Washington, D.C.,
combining a literary career with various types of govern-
ment work. Her home became a famous gathering place for
Negro artists.

Mrs. Johnson's poems are in a distinctly minor key.
A few are deft and musical and fully realized, expressing
strong emotion and "the heart of a woman."

I want to die while you love me,
While yet you hold me fair,
While laughter lies upon my lips
And lights are in my hair.

I want to die while you love me.
I could not bear to see,
The glory of this perfect day,
Grow dim—or cease to be.

I want to die while you love me.
Oh! who would care to live
Till love has nothing more to ask,
And nothing more to give.

I want to die while you love me,
And bear to that still bed
Your kisses, turbulent, unspent,
To warm me when I'm dead.

FENTON JOHNSON
was born in Chicago in 1888 and educated there. He wrote plays and a volume of short stories in addition to several books of verse. Active in Chicago's literary circles, he edited and published several "little" magazines. He died in 1958.

Johnson's early poems, some of them in dialect, are uneven and trite, if not downright amateurish. He is best remembered for his later, more realistic prose poems in the manner of Carl Sandburg. His books are *A Little Dreaming* (1914), *Visions of the Dusk* (1916), *Songs of the Soil* (1916), and the short story collection, *Tales of Darkest America* (1920). An unpublished collection of poems in manuscript is in the Negro Collection of the Fisk University Library.

I am tired of work; I am tired of building up somebody
    else's civilization.

Let us take a rest, M'Lissy Jane.

I will go down to the Last Chance Saloon, drink a gallon
    or two of gin, shoot a game or two of dice and
    sleep the rest of the night on one of Mike's barrels.

You will let the old shanty go to rot, the white people's
    clothes turn to dust, and the Calvary Baptist
    Church sink to the bottomless pit.

You will spend your days forgetting you married me and
    your nights hunting the warm gin Mike serves the
    ladies in the rear of the Last Chance Saloon.

Throw the children into the river; civilization has given
    us too many. It is better to die than it is to grow up
    and find out that you are colored.

Pluck the stars out of the heavens. The stars mark our
    destiny. The stars marked my destiny.

I am tired of civilization.

I mastered pastoral theology, the Greek of the Apostles, and all the difficult subjects in a minister's curriculum.

I was as learned as any in this country when the Bishop ordained me.

And I went to preside over Mount Moriah, largest flock in the Conference.

I preached the Word as I felt it, I visited the sick and dying and comforted the afflicted in spirit.

I loved my work because I loved my God.

But I have lost my charge to Sam Jenkins, who has not been to school four years in his life.

I lost my charge because I could not make my congregation shout. And my dollar money was small, very small.

Sam Jenkins can tear a Bible to tatters and the congregation destroys the pews with their shouting and stamping.

Sam Jenkins leads in the gift of raising dollar money.

Such is religion.

There is music in me, the music of a peasant people.

I wander through the levee, picking my banjo and singing my songs of the cabin and the field. At the Last
Chance Saloon I am as welcome as the violets in
March; there is always food and drink for me
there, and the dimes of those who love honest
music. Behind the railroad tracks the little children clap their hands and love me as they love
Kris Kringle.

But I fear that I am a failure. Last night a woman called
me a troubadour. What is a troubadour?

CLAUDE MC KAY

came to the United States from Jamaica, British West Indies, where he was born in 1891, to study scientific farming. He had already gained some attention as a poet with his first book, *Songs of Jamaica* (1911). He left college after two years and went to New York to devote himself to writing, supporting himself through various menial jobs. In 1920, when he was living in London, his second volume, *Spring in New Hampshire*, was published. Upon his return to New York, he became associate editor of *The Liberator*, a socialist magazine of art and literature. *Harlem Shadows* came out in 1922, his last book of poems until *Selected Poems* (1953), published posthumously. Novelist as well as poet, McKay wrote *Home to Harlem* (1928), his most widely read novel; *Banjo* (1929), and *Banana Bottom*

(1933). His autobiography, *A Long Way from Home,*
appeared in 1937. Illness and destitution made Claude Mc-
Kay's later years difficult, and he died in 1948.

The critical consensus today seems to be that Mc-
Kay's fiction is better on the whole than his poetry. It is
certainly true that a number of his poems are spoiled by
triteness and obvious argument. His lyrics on West Indian
themes, with their frequent note of nostalgia and their exotic images, are often appealing. But these and other poems
echo the diction and manner of late nineteenth-century
poets. Occasionally there is real power in poems voicing
his bitterness as a Negro. Sir Winston Churchill read Mc-
Kay's defiant sonnet, "If We Must Die," to the House of
Commons during World War II, and soldiers are said to
have carried copies of it with them to the battlefield.

SPRING IN NEW HAMPSHIRE

(To J. L. J. F. E.)

Too green the springing April grass,
    Too blue the silver-speckled sky,
For me to linger here, alas,
    While happy winds go laughing by,
Wasting the golden hours indoors,
Washing windows and scrubbing floors.

Too wonderful the April night,
    Too faintly sweet the first May flowers,
The stars too gloriously bright,
    For me to spend the evening hours,
When fields are fresh and streams are leaping,
Wearied, exhausted, dully sleeping.

Bow down my soul in worship very low
And in the holy silences be lost.
Bow down before the marble Man of Woe,
Bow down before the singing angel host.
What jewelled glory fills my spirit's eye,
What golden grandeur moves the depths of me!
The soaring arches lift me up on high,
Taking my breath with their rare symmetry.

Bow down my soul and let the wondrous light
Of beauty bathe thee from her lofty throne,
Bow down before the wonder of man's might.
Bow down in worship, humble and alone,
Bow lowly down before the sacred sight
Of man's Divinity alive in stone.

JEAN TOOMER

was born in Washington, D.C., in 1894. He established himself as one of the most brilliant of the Harlem Renaissance writers with *Cane* (1923), a book of impressionistic stories, sketches, and poems of Southern Negro life. Though it owes something to the fictional technique of the novelist Waldo Frank, Toomer's book is highly original. It has a haunting quality, is richly evocative, and both its prose and poetry are musical and strongly rhythmic. Some of the poems reprinted here are parts of stories and sketches from *Cane,* for which they set a mood or serve as lyrical commentary.

Toomer published relatively little after *Cane* and nothing which equalled that work. Eventually he gave up writing altogether, having beforehand turned away from Negro material. In fact, he ceased to identify himself as a Negro and "crossed the color line."

From KARINTHA

Her skin is like dusk on the eastern horizon,
O cant you see it, O cant you see it,
Her skin is like dusk on the eastern horizon
. . . When the sun goes down.

REAPERS

Black reapers with the sound of steel on stones
Are sharpening scythes. I see them place the hones
In their hip-pockets as a thing that's done,
And start their silent swinging, one by one.
Black horses drive a mower through the weeds,
And there, a field rat, startled, squealing bleeds,
His belly close to ground. I see the blade,
Blood-stained, continue cutting weeds and shade.

From CARMA

Wind is in the cane. Come along.
Cane leaves swaying, rusty with talk,
Scratching choruses above the guinea's squawk,
Wind is in the cane. Come along.

Pour O pour that parting soul in song,
O pour it in the sawdust glow of night,
Into the velvet pine-smoke air to-night,
And let the valley carry it along.
And let the valley carry it along.

O land and soil, red soil and sweet-gum tree,
So scant of grass, so profligate of pines,
Now just before an epoch's sun declines
Thy son, in time, I have returned to thee,
Thy son, I have in time returned to thee.

In time, for though the sun is setting on
A song-lit race of slaves, it has not set;
Though late, O soil, it is not too late yet
To catch thy plaintive soul, leaving, soon gone,
Leaving, to catch thy plaintive soul soon gone.

O Negro slaves, dark purple ripened plums,
Squeezed, and bursting in the pine-wood air,
Passing, before they stripped the old tree bare
One plum was saved for me, one seed becomes

An everlasting song, a singing tree,
Caroling softly souls of slavery,
What they were, and what they are to me,
Caroling softly souls of slavery.

The sky, lazily disdaining to pursue
    The setting sun, too indolent to hold
    A lengthened tournament for flashing gold,
Passively darkens for night's barbecue,

A feast of moon and men and barking hounds,
    An orgy for some genius of the South
    With blood-shot eyes and cane-lipped scented mouth,
Surprised in making folk-songs from soul sounds.

The sawmill blows its whistle, buzz-saws stop,
    And silence breaks the bud of knoll and hill,
    Soft settling pollen where plowed lands fulfill
Their early promise of a bumper crop.

Smoke from the pyramidal sawdust pile
    Curls up, blue ghosts of trees, tarrying low
    Where only chips and stumps are left to show
The solid proof of former domicile.

Meanwhile, the men, with vestiges of pomp,
    Race memories of king and caravan,
    High-priests, an ostrich, and a juju-man,
Go singing through the footpaths of the swamp.

Their voices rise . . . the pine trees are guitars,
    Strumming, pine-needles fall like sheets of rain . . .
    Their voices rise . . . the chorus of the cane
Is caroling a vesper to the stars . . .

O singers, resinous and soft your songs
    Above the sacred whisper of the pines,
    Give virgin lips to cornfield concubines,
Bring dreams of Christ to dusky cane-lipped throngs.

☞ MELVIN B. TOLSON
was hailed as a major poet on the appearance of his last book, *Harlem Gallery*, in 1965. Born in Moberly, Missouri, in 1900, he was educated at Fisk, Lincoln, and Columbia Universities. He taught at various Southern colleges before settling at Langston University, Oklahoma, where he remained for several decades and became Professor of Creative Literature. Besides directing the campus Dust Bowl Theater, he was active in the political life of his community and served four terms as mayor of Langston. In spite of all the demands on his time, Tolson continued to write poems, and a group of lyrics, "Dark Symphony," won the poetry contest sponsored by the America Negro Exposition in Chicago. Commissioned to write a poem for the Liberian Centennial and International Exposition, he published *Libretto*

for the Republic of Liberia in 1953. He received various awards and prizes for his poetry. At the time of his death in 1966, he was Writer in Residence at Tuskegee Institute. He was widely known as a colorful "platform personality" and as a unique storyteller, conversationalist, and reader of his poems. Besides the two books cited, he was the author of *Rendezvous with America* (1944).

If Tolson's poetry shows considerable intellectual range, energetic imagination, skillful melding of disparate materials, it also displays the poet's deliberate attempt to be "modern." His poetry often strikes one as being too intricate, erudite, and obscure. There is a certain cosmopolitanism in Tolson's verse; there is also the consciousness, expressed very often with ironic humor, of what it means to be a Negro in the Western World.

I

A connoisseur of pearl
necklace phrases,
Wu Shang disdains
his laundry, lazes
among his bric-a-brac
metaphysical;
and yet dark customers,
on Harlem's rack
quizzical,
sweat and pack
the forked caldera of
his Stygian shop:
some worship God,
and some Be-Bop.

Wu Shang discovers
the diademed word to be,
on the sly,
a masterkey
to Harlem pocketbooks,
outjockeyed by
policy
and brimstone
theology
alone!

As bust and hips
her corset burst,
An Amazonian fantasy,
A Witness of Jehovah
by job and husband curst,
lumbers in.
A yellow mummy in a mummery
a tip-toe,
Wu Shang unsheathes a grin,
and then, his fingers sleeved,
gulps an ugh and eats his crow,
disarmed by ugliness disbelieved!

At last he takes his wits
from balls of moth,
salaams. "Dear Lady, I, for you,
wear goats' sackcloth
to mark this hour and place;
cursed be the shadow of delay
that for a trice conceals a trace
of beauty in thy face!"

Her jug of anger emptied, now he sighs:
"Her kind cannot play euchre.
The master trick belongs to him
who holds the joker."
His mind's eye sees a black hand drop
a red white poker.

III
The gingered gigolo,
vexed by the harrow of a date

and vanity torn,
goddamns the yellow sage,
four million yellow born,
and yellow fate!

The gigolo
a wayward bronco
seen but unheard,
Wu Shang applies the curb-bit word:
"Wise lovers know
that in their lottery success
belongs to him who plays a woman
with titbits of a guess."

The sweet man's sportive whack
Paralyzes Wu Shang's back.
"Say, Yellah Boy, I call yo' stuff
the hottest dope in town!
That red hot mama'll never know
she got her daddy down."

IV
Sometimes the living dead
stalk in and sue for grace,
the tragic uncommon
in the comic commonplace,
the evil that the good
begets in love's embrace,
a Harlem melodrama
like that in Big John's face

as Wu Shang peers at him
and cudgels a theorem.

The sage says in a voice ilang-ilang,
"Do you direct the weathercock?"
And then his lash, a rackarock,
descends with a bang,
"Show me the man who has not thrown
a boomerang!"

. . . words, no longer pearls,
but drops of Gilead's balm.
Later, later, Wu Shang remarks,
"Siroccos mar the toughest palm."
The bigger thing, as always, goes unsaid:
the look behind the door of Big John's eyes,
awareness of the steps of *Is,*
the freedom of the wise.

V

When Dixie Dixon breaks a leg
on arctic Lenox Avenue
and Wu Shang homes her, pays her fees,
old kismet knots the two
unraveled destinies.
The unperfumed
wag foot, forefinger, head;
and belly laughter waifs ghost rats
foxed by the smells of meat and bread;
and black walls blab, "Good Gawd,
China and Africa gits wed!"

VI

Wu Shang, whom nothing sears,
says Dixie is a dusky passion flower
unsoiled by envious years.

And Dixie says
her Wu Shang is a Mandarin
with seven times seven ways of love,
her very own oasis in
the desert
of Harlem men.

In dignity, Wu Shang and Dixie walk
the gauntlet, Lenox Avenue;
their son has Wu Shang's cast
and Dixie's hue.

The dusky children roll
their oyster eyes
at Wu Shang, Junior, flash
a premature surmise,
as if afraid:
in accents Carolina
on the streets they never made,
the dusky children tease,
"African China!"

Strange but true is the story
of the sea-turtle and the shark—
the instinctive drive of the weak to survive
in the oceanic dark.
Driven,
riven
by hunger
from abyss to shoal,
sometimes the shark swallows
the sea-turtle whole.
"The sly reptilian marine
withdraws,
into the shell
of his undersea craft,
his leathery head and the rapacious claws
that can rip
a rhinoceros' hide
or strip
a crocodile to fare-thee-well;
now,
inside the shark,
the sea-turtle begins the churning seesaws
of his descent into pelagic hell;
then . . . *then,*
with ravenous jaws
that can cut sheet steel scrap,
the sea-turtle gnaws
. . . and gnaws . . . and gnaws . . .
his way in a way that appalls—
his way to freedom,
beyond the vomiting dark,
beyond the stomach walls
of the shark."

FRANK HORNE

has had a series of distinguished careers as a college athlete, an optometrist, and an official with the United States Housing Authority. He is also notable for his work in the field of race relations. He was born in New York City in 1899, and is the uncle of Lena Horne, the stage and screen star.

Horne's most frequently anthologized poems are the series, "Letters Found Near a Suicide," awarded *The Crisis* poetry prize in 1925. Irony and satire, faith as well as skepticism, operate in his work, and he can be terse and hard-boiled. His *Haverstraw,* containing, among others, poems recording the physical and spiritual effects of a serious illness, was brought out by Paul Breman in London in 1962.

TO JAMES

Do you remember
How you won
That last race . . . ?
How you flung your body
At the start . . .
How your spikes
Ripped the cinders
In the stretch . . .
How you catapulted
Through the tape . . .
Do you remember . . . ?
Don't you think
I lurched with you
Out of those starting holes . . . ?
Don't you think
My sinews tightened
At those first
Few strides . . .
And when you flew into the stretch
Was not all my thrill
Of a thousand races
In your blood . . . ?
At your final drive
Through the finish line
Did not my shout
Tell of the

Triumphant ecstasy
Of victory . . . ?
Live
As I have taught you
To run, Boy—
It's a short dash
Dig your starting holes
Deep and firm
Lurch out of them
Into the straightaway
With all the power
That is in you
Look straight ahead
To the finish line
Think only of the goal
Run straight
Run high
Run hard
Save nothing
And finish
With an ecstatic burst
That carries you
Hurtling
Through the tape
To victory . . .

KID STUFF

DECEMBER, *1942*
The wise guys
tell me
that Christmas
is Kid Stuff . . .
Maybe they've got
something there—
Two thousand years ago
three wise guys
chased a star
across a continent
to bring
frankincense and myrrh
to a Kid
born in a manger
with an idea in his head . . .

And as the bombs
crash
all over the world
today
the real wise guys
know
that we've all
got to go chasing stars
again
in the hope
that we can get back
some of that
Kid Stuff
born two thousand years ago.

STERLING A. BROWN
has found in Negro folklore and folk experience the chief
sources of his poetry; indeed, he is an authority on jazz and
Negro folklore. *Southern Road* (1932) contains poems in
the spirit and idiom of blues and work songs, of ballads and
tall tales. Brown makes frequent use of dialect, but since
he is a social realist his poems in this medium are not sentimental, and their humor can have a sharp edge, as in the
"Slim Greer" series. He is no creator of Dixie pastorals, except in a wholly ironic sense. Protest, sometimes explicit,
sometimes implicit, gives impetus to many of his pieces, but
protest is only one aspect of his writing; he also has a flair
for comedy. A fine craftsman, he composes both in free
verse and formal patterns. His sonnets and personal lyrics
are skillfully executed, if somewhat less forceful than his
other poems.

Brown was born in Washington, D.C., in 1901. He has taught English at Howard University there for a number of years and has been visiting professor at New York University, Atlanta University, and Vassar College. In 1937 he received a Guggenheim Fellowship for creative writing. He was Editor on Negro Affairs for the Federal Writers Project, 1938–39, and was a resourceful contributor to the Carnegie-Myrdal Study of the Negro in 1939. His poems and articles have been in a variety of magazines and anthologies. An astute critic, he has produced two books of criticism, both issued in 1938, *The Negro in American Fiction* and *Negro Poetry and Drama*. He was the senior editor of *The Negro Caravan* (1941), an anthology that remains the best of its kind.

Mose is black and evil
And damns his luck
Driving Mister Schwartz's
Big coal truck.

He's got no gal,
He's got no jack,
No fancy silk shirts
For his back.

But summer evenings,
Hard luck Mose
Goes in for all
The fun he knows.

On the corner kerb
With a sad quartette
His tenor peals
Like a clarinet.

O hit it Moses
Sing att thing
But Mose's mind
Goes wandering;—

And to the stars
Over the town
Floats, from a good man
Way, way down—

A soft song, filled
With a misery
Older than Mose
Will ever be.

One thing you left with us, Jack Johnson.
One thing before they got you.

You used to stand there like a man,
Taking punishment
With a golden, spacious grin;
Confident.
Inviting big Jim Jeffries, who was boring in:
"Heah ah is, big boy; yuh sees whah Ise at.
Come on in. . . ."

Thanks, Jack, for that.

John Henry, with your hammer;
John Henry, with your steel driver's pride,
You taught us that a man could go down like a man,
Sticking to your hammer till you died.
Sticking to your hammer till you died.

Brother,
When, beneath the burning sun
The sweat poured down and the breath came thick,
And the loaded hammer swung like a ton
And the heart grew sick;
You had what we need now, John Henry.
Help us get it.

So if we go down
Have to go down
We go like you, brother,
'Nachal' men. . . .

Old nameless couple in Red River Bottom,
Who have seen floods gutting out your best loam,
And the boll weevil chase you
Out of your hard-earned home,
Have seen the drought parch your green fields,
And the cholera stretch your porkers out dead;
Have seen year after year
The commissary always a little in the lead;

Even you said
That which we need
Now in our time of fear,—
Routed your own deep misery and dread,
Muttering, beneath an unfriendly sky,
"Guess we'll give it one mo' try.
Guess we'll give it one mo' try."

REVELATIONS

"Why do folks call you Revelations?"
"It used to be because I preached from that Book. But now
    because I reveals."

TALKS WITH THE VILLAGE HALFWIT

I shall recall
As a sinister omen,
That which was pity
For full-bosomed women,—

      That which was laughter
      For idling men;
      Bundle of rags,
      And tattered brain,

Cadaverous cheeks,
And bloodshot eyes,
And wide mouth mumbling
Obscenities,

      Or echoes from childhood's
      Store of rhyme,
      Or scraps of religion
      Near sublime. . . .

I shall remember
Troubledly, long,
His cracked voice
Wheezing out his song:

74

"You gotta walk that lonesome valley,
You gotta walk it by yo'self,
Nobody heah can a-walk it for you
You gotta walk it by yo-self."

And this comment
From wisdom not his own
    "Man wanta live,
    Man wanta find himself
    Man gotta learn
    How to go alone."

Always now with me
The halfwit's text,
Sour truth for my wits
Poor, perplexed,

    "If man's life goes
    Beyond the bone
    Man must go lonely
    And alone,
    Unhelped, unhindered
    On his own. . . ."

Good glory, give a look at Sporting Beasley
Strutting, oh my Lord.

Tophat cocked one side his bulldog head,
Striped four-in-hand, and in his buttonhole
A red carnation; Prince Albert coat
Form-fitting, corset like; vest snugly filled,
Gray morning trousers, spotless and full-flowing,
White spats and a cane.

Step it, Mr. Beasley, oh step it till the sun goes down.

Forget the snippy clerks you wait upon,
Tread clouds of glory above the heads of pointing
children,
Oh, Mr. Peacock, before the drab barnfowl of the
world.

Forget the laughter when at the concert
You paced down the aisle, your majesty,
Down to Row A, where you pulled out your opera
glasses.

Majesty. . . .

It's your turn now, Sporting Beasley,
Step it off.
The world is a ragbag; the world
Is full of heathens who haven't seen the light;
Do it, Mr. Missionary.

Great glory, give a look.

Oh Jesus, when this brother's bill falls due,
When he steps off the chariot
And flicks the dust from his patent leathers with his
    silk handkerchief,
When he stands in front of the jasper gates, patting
    his tie,

And then paces in
Cane and knees working like well-oiled slow-timed
    pistons;

Lord help us, give a *look* at him.

Don't make him dress up in no night gown, Lord.
Don't put no fuss and feathers on his shoulders, Lord.

Let him know it's heaven.

Let him keep his hat, his vest, his elkstooth, and
    everything.

Let him have his spats and cane
Let him have his spats and cane

has produced a large body of work, including novels, short stories, biographies, children's books (for which he has received awards), anthologies, and a volume of poetry, *Personals* (London, 1964).

He was born in Alexandria, Louisiana, in 1902. After completing his studies at Pacific Union College in 1923, he went to New York, and there he put aside his earlier ambition to become a doctor and began his writing career. He gained attention as one of the poets of the Harlem Renaissance. His first novel, *God Sends Sunday,* was published in 1931. Two children's books and two more novels, *Black Thunder* and *Drums at Dusk,* followed within the next few years. In 1938 he was granted a Rosenwald Fellowship. He later studied library science at the University of Chicago, becoming chief librarian at Fisk University in 1943, a post he held until his resignation in 1965, when he assumed duties in the university's public relations office. He has been a Guggenheim Fellow. He was co-editor with Langston Hughes of *The Poetry of the Negro* (1950) and has edited *American Negro Poetry* (1963) and other anthologies.

Bontemps is better known today as a prose writer than as a poet. But his love of poetry remains undiminished, as evidenced by the anthologies he has published and by the fact that over the years he has given strategic help to a number of struggling poets. His poems, the majority of them written during the 1920's, lack incisiveness but are reflective, musical, and aptly phrased, informed by an appealing lyricism, often by an engaging youthfulness of spirit.

Go through the gates with closed eyes.
Stand erect and let your black face front the west.
Drop the axe and leave the timber where it lies;
A woodman on the hill must have his rest.

Go where leaves are lying brown and wet.
Forget her warm arms and her breast who mothered you,
And every face you ever loved forget.
Close your eyes; walk bravely through.

SOUTHERN MANSION

Poplars are standing there still as death
And ghosts of dead men
Meet their ladies walking
Two by two beneath the shade
And standing on the marble steps.

There is a sound of music echoing
Through the open door
And in the field there is
Another sound tinkling in the cotton:
Chains of bondmen dragging on the ground.

The years go back with an iron clank,
A hand is on the gate,
A dry leaf trembles on the wall.
Ghosts are walking.
They have broken roses down
And poplars stand there still as death.

After the cloud embankments,
The lamentation of wind,
And the starry descent into time,
We came to the flashing waters and shaded our eyes
From the glare.

Alone with the shore and the harbor,
The stems of the cocoanut trees,
The fronds of silence and hushed music,
We cried for the new revelation
And waited for miracles to rise.

Where elements touch and merge,
Where shadows swoon like outcasts on the sand
And the tired moment waits, its courage gone—
There were we

In latitudes where storms are born.

The hills are wroth; the stones have scored you bitterly
because you looked upon the naked sun
oblivious of them, because you did not see
the trees you touched or mountains that you walked
    upon.

But there will come a day of darkness in the land,
a day wherein remembered sun alone comes through
to mark the hills; then perhaps you'll understand
just how it was you drew from them and they from you.

For there will be a bent old woman in that day
who, feeling something of this country in her bones,
will leave her house tapping with a stick, who will (they
    say)
come back to seek the girl she was in these familiar
    stones.

I have sown beside all waters in my day.
I planted deep, within my heart the fear
That wind or fowl would take the grain away.
I planted safe against this stark, lean year.

I scattered seed enough to plant the land
In rows from Canada to Mexico,
But for my reaping only what the hand
Can hold at once is all that I can show.

Yet what I sowed and what the orchard yields
My brother's sons are gathering stalk and root,
Small wonder then my children glean in fields
They have not sown, and feed on bitter fruit.

LANGSTON HUGHES

has an international reputation. His books have been translated into all the major languages, his plays performed in many countries. He has been popularly called "poet laureate of the Negro race." During a career spanning more than forty years, Hughes produced novels, collections of short stories, biographies, children's books, translations, opera librettos, and poetry—and this list is far from complete. When he died in May, 1967, he had the distinction of being one of the only American Negro men of letters able to support himself by his writing.

Hughes was born in Joplin, Missouri, in 1902, and received his public school education in Lawrence, Kansas, and Cleveland, Ohio. He attended Columbia University for a year before going to sea in 1922 as a sailor on a freighter whose ports of call were the Canary Islands, the Azores, and West Africa. Two years later, he was in Paris earning a meagre living as cook and doorman.

Upon his return to the United States, he went to Washington, and while a bus boy in a hotel met the famous poet, Vachel Lindsay. Lindsay was so excited by the poems Hughes ventured to show him that he included some of them in a public reading. Newspapers carried the story of Lindsay's "discovery." In 1925, Hughes, by now associated with the Harlem Renaissance writers, won first prize in the *Opportunity* poetry contest. *The Weary Blues,* his first book of poems, was published the next year. He resumed his interrupted formal education at Lincoln University, and before being graduated in 1929 had won the Witter

Bynner Prize for poetry and had written a novel, *Not Without Laughter*, which was published in 1930 and brought him the Harmon Gold Award in 1931. After that, books and honors proliferated. He was granted a Guggenheim Fellowship in 1935. He received the Spingarn Medal in 1960 and was elected to the American Academy of Arts and Letters in 1961.

Notable among the thirty or more books he wrote are *The Big Sea* and *I Wonder as I Wander,* in which he recounted with zest and refreshing humor the engrossing story of his career as writer and world-traveler. Among the many books of poetry he published are *Fine Clothes to the Jew* (1927), *Dear Lovely Death* (1931), *Shakespeare in Harlem* (1941), *Selected Poems* (1959), and *Ask Your Mama: Twelve Moods for Jazz* (1961). He was co-editor with Arna Bontemps of *The Poetry of the Negro* (1950) and edited *New Negro Poets: U.S.A.* (1964).

As a young poet of the Harlem Renaissance, Langston Hughes showed in his work a feeling for the rhythms of jazz, an interest in Negro folk expression, and social awareness. These are still characteristic in his later work. His vision of life is positive, fundamentally joyous, though it encompasses anguish, too, and is expressed in verse that often gives the effect of spontaneous utterance, of improvisation. Herein lie both his strength and his weakness as a poet, since his poems, though affording quick, vivid impressions or insights, are not always as carefully worked out as they might have been.

I, too, sing America.

I am the darker brother.
They send me to eat in the kitchen
When company comes,
But I laugh,
And eat well,
And grow strong.

Tomorrow,
I'll be at the table
When company comes.
Nobody'll dare
Say to me,
"Eat in the kitchen,"
Then.

Besides,
They'll see how beautiful I am
And be ashamed—

I, too, am America.

Jazzonia

Oh, silver tree!
Oh, shining rivers of the soul.

In a Harlem cabaret
Six long-headed jazzers play.
A dancing girl whose eyes are bold
Lifts high a dress of silken gold.

Oh, singing tree!
Oh, shining rivers of the soul!

Were Eve's eyes
In the first garden
Just a bit too bold?
Was Cleopatra gorgeous
In a gown of gold?

Oh, shining tree!
Oh, silver rivers of the soul!

In a whirling cabaret
Six long-headed jazzers play.

The Pennsylvania Station in New York
Is like some vast basilica of old
That towers above the terrors of the dark
As bulwark and protection to the soul.
Now people who are hurrying alone
And those who come in crowds from far away
Pass through this great concourse of steel and stone
To trains, or else from trains out into day.
And as in great basilicas of old
The search was ever for a dream of God,
So here the search is still within each soul
Some seed to find that sprouts a holy tree
To glorify the earth—and you—and me.

I

Oh, God of dust and rainbows, help us see
That without dust the rainbow would not be.

II

I look with awe upon the human race
And God, Who sometimes spits right in its face.

Pigalle:
A neon rose
In a champagne bottle.
At dawn
The petals
Fall.

Anybody
Better than
Nobody.

In the barren dusk
Even the snake
That spirals
Terror on the sand—

Better than nobody
In this lonely
Land.

When the cold comes
With a bitter fragrance
Like rusty iron and mint,
And the wind blows
Fresh and sharp as integration
With an edge like gentle apartheid,
And it is winter,
And the cousins of the too thin suits
Ride on bitless horses
Tethered by something worse than pride,
Which areaway, or bar,
Or station waiting room will not say,
Horse and horseman, outside!
With old and not too gentle
Colorless apartheid?

The street light
On its lonely arm
Becomes
An extension
Of the Cross—
The Cross itself
A lonely arm
Whose light is lost.

Oh, lonely world!
Oh, lonely light!
Oh, lonely Cross!

☙ COUNTEE CULLEN
was born in New York City in 1903 and, except for so-
journs abroad, lived there all his life. His first collection of
poems, *Color,* was published in 1925, while he was an un-
dergraduate at New York University. This book brought
acclaim to the young poet as an extraordinarily gifted lyr-
ist, and he received the Harmon Gold Award. He had already won other literary prizes, among them the Witter
Bynner Poetry Prize. A brilliant student, he was elected to
Phi Beta Kappa in his senior year. He went to Harvard for
his M.A. degree, and there came under the influence of the
poet Robert Hillyer, to whom Cullen dedicated a group of
lyrics in *Copper Sun* (1927). After graduation from Harvard, he became assistant editor of *Opportunity,* and his
reputation continued to grow.

The Black Christ (1929), written in Paris on a
Guggenheim Fellowship, was followed by a novel, *One
Way to Heaven* (1932), *The Medea and Other Poems*
(1935), and *The Lost Zoo* (1940), a highly imaginative
book of poems for children. In 1934 Cullen became a
teacher of English and French at Frederick Douglass Junior High School, beginning a new career that conflicted in

many ways with his own creative work, but which he pursued with distinction. Other books are *The Ballad of the Brown Girl*, brought out in a special edition in 1927; *Caroling Dusk* (1927), an anthology of poems by Negro poets; and *My Lives and How I Lost Them* (1942), stories for children. He collaborated with his friend Arna Bontemps on a Broadway musical based on the latter's novel, *God Sends Sunday*. Cullen died prematurely in 1946, and his collected poems, *On These I Stand*, were published the following year.

Poems on racial themes form a significant part of Cullen's work, but they cannot in all fairness be considered more important than those in which he gave lyric expression to the universals of human experience. He was conservative in outlook, conventional rather than experimental in technique. He acknowledged Keats as a central influence and showed some artistic kinship with A. E. Housman and Edna St. Vincent Millay. Although he felt the obligation to speak out against prejudice and bigotry, he avoided obvious propaganda. At his best Cullen was, as one critic put it, "sheer poet."

With two white roses on her breasts,
    White candles at head and feet,
Dark Madonna of the grave she rests;
    Lord Death has found her sweet.

Her mother pawned her wedding ring
    To lay her out in white;
She'd be so proud she'd dance and sing
    To see herself tonight.

TABLEAU

(For Donald Duff)

Locked arm in arm they cross the way,
    The black boy and the white,
The golden splendor of the day,
    The sable pride of night.

From lowered blinds the dark folk stare,
    And here the fair folk talk,
Indignant that these two should dare
    In unison to walk.

Oblivious to look and word
    They pass, and see no wonder
That lightning brilliant as a sword
    Should blaze the path of thunder.

Some are teethed on a silver spoon,
    With the stars strung for a rattle;
I cut my teeth as the black raccoon—
    For implements of battle.

Some are swaddled in silk and down,
    And heralded by a star;
They swathed my limbs in a sackcloth gown
    On a night that was black as tar.

For some, godfather and goddame
    The opulent fairies be;
Dame Poverty gave me my name,
    And Pain godfathered me.

For I was born on Saturday—
    "Bad time for planting a seed,"
Was all my father had to say,
    And, "One mouth more to feed."

Death cut the strings that gave me life,
    And handed me to Sorrow,
The only kind of middle wife
    My folks could beg or borrow.

Now I am young and credulous,
    My heart is quick to bleed
At courage in the tremulous
    Slow sprouting of a seed.

Now I am young and sensitive,
    Man's lack can stab me through;
I own no stitch I would not give
    To him that asked me to.

Now I am young and a fool for love,
    My blood goes mad to see
A brown girl pass me like a dove
    That flies melodiously.

Let me be lavish of my tears,
    And dream that false is true;
Though wisdom cometh with the years,
    The barren days come, too.

She even thinks that up in heaven
    Her class lies late and snores,
While poor black cherubs rise at seven
    To do celestial chores.

FOR JOHN KEATS

(Apostle of Beauty)

Not writ in water, nor in mist,
    Sweet lyric throat, thy name;
Thy singing lips that cold death kissed
    Have seared his own with flame.

Born of the sorrowful of heart,
    Mirth was a crown upon his head;
Pride kept his twisted lips apart
    In jest, to hide a heart that bled.

FROM THE DARK TOWER

(To Charles S. Johnson)

We shall not always plant while others reap
The golden increment of bursting fruit,
Not always countenance, abject and mute,
That lesser men should hold their brothers cheap;
Not everlastingly while others sleep
Shall we beguile their limbs with mellow flute,
Not always bend to some more subtle brute;
We were not made eternally to weep.

The night whose sable breast relieves the stark,
White stars is no less lovely being dark,
And there are buds that cannot bloom at all
In light, but crumble, piteous, and fall;
So in the dark we hide the heart that bleeds,
And wait, and tend our agonizing seeds.

FRANK MARSHALL DAVIS, now living with his family in Hawaii, was born in Arkansas City, Kansas, in 1905. He studied journalism at Kansas City College and was for a long period affiliated with the United Negro Press in Chicago. In 1937 he received a Rosenwald Fellowship for creative writing.

Davis's poems are in free verse, and are characterized by realism and satire in the service of racial protest and the denunciation of social evils. His books are *Black Man's Verse* (1935), *I Am the American Negro* (1937), and *47th Street* (1948).

Having attained success in business
possessing three cars
one wife and two mistresses
a home and furniture
talked of by the town
and thrice ruler of the local Elks
Robert Whitmore
died of apoplexy
when a stranger from Georgia
mistook him
for a former Macon waiter.

ARTHUR RIDGEWOOD, M.D.

He debated whether
as a poet
to have dreams and beans
or as a physician
have a long car and caviar.
Dividing his time between both
he died from a nervous breakdown
caused by worry
from rejection slips
and final notices from the finance company.

GILES JOHNSON, PH.D.

Giles Johnson
had four college degrees
knew the whyfore of this
the wherefore of that
could orate in Latin
or cuss in Greek
and, having learned such things
he died of starvation
because he wouldn't teach
and he couldn't porter.

ROBERT HAYDEN

was born in Detroit, Michigan, in 1913. He did his under-graduate work at Wayne State University and earned his M.A. degree at the University of Michigan, where he subsequently taught English for two years. In 1946 he joined the faculty of Fisk University and is now Professor of English there.

His poetry has brought him several fellowships and prizes, among them The Hopwood Award from the University of Michigan in 1938 and again in 1942, a Rosenwald Fellowship in 1947, and a Ford Foundation grant in 1954. His book, *A Ballad of Remembrance,* published in a limited edition in London by Paul Breman in 1962, won The Grand Prize for Poetry at The First World Festival of Negro Arts held in Dakar, Senegal, in 1965. Hayden has been the editor and publisher of The Counterpoise Series, presenting work by Myron O'Higgins, Alvin C. Cooper, Margaret Danner, and himself. He is poetry editor of the Baha'i magazine *World Order.* Besides *A Ballad of Remembrance,* his books are *Heart-Shape in the Dust* (1940) and *Selected Poems* (1966).

Hayden is interested in Negro history and folklore and has written poems using materials from these sources. Opposed to the chauvinistic and the doctrinaire, he sees no reason why a Negro poet should be limited to "racial utterance" or to having his writing judged by standards different from those applied to the work of other poets.

Sank through easeful
azure. Flower
creatures flashed and
shimmered there—
lost images
fadingly remembered.
Swiftly descended
into canyon of cold
nightgreen emptiness.
Freefalling, weightless
as in dreams of
wingless flight,
plunged through infra-
space and came to
the dead ship,
carcass that swarmed with
voracious life.
Angelfish, their
lively blue and
yellow prised from
darkness by the
flashlight's beam,
thronged her portholes.
Moss of bryozoans
blurred, obscured her
metal. Snappers,

gold groupers explored her,
fearless of bubbling
manfish. I entered
the wreck, awed by her silence,
feeling more keenly
the iron cold.
With flashlight probing
fogs of water
saw the sad slow
dance of gilded
chairs, the ectoplasmic
swirl of garments,
drowned instruments
of buoyancy,
drunken shoes. Then
livid gesturings,
eldritch hide and
seek of laughing
faces. I yearned to
find those hidden
ones, to fling aside
the mask and call to them,
yield to rapturous
whisperings, have
done with self and
every dinning
vain complexity.
Yet in languid
frenzy strove, as
one freezing fights off
sleep desiring sleep;
strove against the
cancelling arms that

suddenly surrounded
me, fled the numbing
kisses that I craved.
Reflex of life-wish?
Respirator's brittle
belling? Swam from
the ship somehow;
somehow began the
measured rise.

No longer throne of a goddess to whom we pray,
no longer the bubble house of childhood's
tumbling Mother Goose man,

The emphatic moon ascends—
the brilliant challenger of rocket experts,
the white hope of communications men.

Some I love who are dead
were watchers of the moon and knew its lore;
planted seeds, trimmed their hair,

Pierced their ears for gold hoop earrings
as it waxed or waned.
It shines tonight upon their graves.

And burned in the garden of Gethsemane,
its light made holy by the dazzling tears
with which it mingled.

And spread its radiance on the exile's path
of Him who was The Glorious One,
its light made holy by His holiness.

Already a mooted goal and tomorrow perhaps
an arms base, a livid sector,
the full moon dominates the dark.

THE BALLAD OF SUE ELLEN WESTERFIELD

(For Clyde)

She grew up in bedeviled southern wilderness,
but had not been a slave, she said,
because her father wept and set her mother free.
She hardened in perilous rivertowns
and after The Surrender,
went as maid upon the tarnished Floating Palaces.
Rivermen reviled her for the rankling cold
sardonic pride
that gave a knife-edge to her comeliness.

When she was old, her back still straight,
her hair still glossy black,
she'd talk sometimes
of dangers lived through on the rivers.
But never told of him,
whose name she'd vowed she would not speak again
till after Jordan.
Oh, he was nearer nearer now
than wearisome kith and kin.
His blue eyes followed her
as she moved about her tasks upon the *Memphis Rose.*
He smiled and joshed, his voice quickening her.
She cursed the circumstance. . . .

The crazing horrors of that summer night,
the swifting flames, he fought his way to her,

the savaging panic, and helped her swim to shore.
The steamer like besieged Atlanta blazing,
the cries, the smoke and bellowing flames,
the flamelit thrashing forms in hellmouth water,
and he swimming out to them,
leaving her dazed and lost.
A woman screaming under the raddled trees—
Sue Ellen felt it was herself who screamed.
The moaning of the hurt, the terrified—
she held off shuddering despair
and went to comfort whom she could.
Wagons torches bells
and whimpering dusk of morning
and blankness lostness nothingness for her
until his arms had lifted her
into wild and secret dark.

How long how long was it they wandered,
loving fearing loving,
fugitives whose dangerous only hidingplace
was love?
How long was it before she knew
she could not forfeit what she was,
even for him—could not, even for him,
forswear her pride?
They kissed and said farewell at last.
He wept as had her father once.
They kissed and said farewell.
Until her dying-bed,
she cursed the circumstance.

Nobody planted roses, he recalls,
but sunflowers gangled there sometimes,
tough-stalked and bold
and like the vivid children there unplanned.
There circus-poster horses curveted
in trees of heaven
above the quarrels and shattered glass,
and he was bareback rider of them all.

No roses there in summer—
oh, never roses except when people died—
and no vacations for his elders,
so harshened after each unrelenting day
that they were shouting-angry.
But summer was, they said, the poor folks' time
of year. And he remembers
how they would sit on broken steps amid

The fevered tossings of the dusk, the dark,
wafting hearsay with funeral-parlor fans
or making evening solemn by
their quietness. Feels their Mosaic eyes
upon him, though the florist roses
that only sorrow could afford
long since have bidden them Godspeed.

Oh, summer summer summertime—

Then grim street preachers shook
their tambourines and Bibles in the face
of tolerant wickedness;
then Elks parades and big splendiferous
Jack Johnson in his diamond limousine
set the ghetto burgeoning
with fantasies
of Ethiopia spreading her gorgeous wings.

When it is finally ours, this freedom, this liberty, this
        beautiful
and terrible thing, needful to man as air,
usable as earth; when it belongs at last to all,
when it is truly instinct, brain matter, diastole, systole,
reflex action; when it is finally won; when it is more
than the gaudy mumbo jumbo of politicians:
this man, this Douglass, this former slave, this Negro
beaten to his knees, exiled, visioning a world
where none is lonely, none hunted, alien,
this man, superb in love and logic, this man
shall be remembered. Oh, not with statues' rhetoric,
not with legends and poems and wreaths of bronze alone,
but with the lives grown out of his life, the lives
fleshing his dream of the beautiful, needful thing.

OWEN DODSON

was born in Brooklyn in 1914 and educated at Bates College and Yale University. He has published two novels and a book of poems, *Powerful Long Ladder* (1946). His verse plays, *Divine Comedy* and *Garden of Time,* have been performed at Yale and elsewhere. His productions of plays at Howard University, where he is chairman of the Drama Department, have earned him a reputation as an outstanding director. In 1949 he took the Howard University Players, sponsored by The State Department, on a successful tour of Scandinavia and Germany. He has been a Rosenwald Fellow, and in 1953 he went to Italy on a Guggenheim grant for a year of writing. He has received the *Paris Review* short story prize and the Maxwell Anderson Verse Play award.

Dodson has an ear for the rhythms of Negro folk speech, and has written effective poems in this idiom. His personal lyrics express strong emotion and, not infrequently, spiritual conflict. When they fail, their failure is due to imprecision of image or phrase. In recent years Dodson has been writing religious verse that at times successfully blends the mystical and the familiar.

CIRCLE ONE

(For Gordon Heath)

Nothing happens only once,
Nothing happens only here,
Every love that lies asleep
Wakes today another year.

Why we sailed and how we prosper
Will be sung and lived again;
All the lands repeat themselves,
Shore for shore and men for men.

Now would I tread my darkness down
And wish for clover overhead;
The roots below will twine a crown
When I am dead.

The seal of color stamps too deep
For wounded flesh to live and win;
The earth is shielding and will keep
My darkness close within.

"They got pictures of V stamped on letter stamps;
Miss Eagle wear one in her lapel to her Red Cross suit;
Mr. Bigful, the bank president, got one in his lapel too;
Some of the people I do laundry with got great big ones
    in they windows;
Hadley Brothers Department Store uptown got pictures
    of V on they store-bought dresses,
Even got a V ice-cream dish—girls selling them so fast
    had to run up a sign: NO MORE V SUNDAES;
And bless God, Lucy done gone up North and come
    back with one gleaming on her pocketbook.
Now let's get this straight: what do them V's mean?"
"V stands for Victory."
"Now just what is this here Victory?"
"It what we get when we fight for it."
"Ought to be Freedom, God do know that!"

HYMN WRITTEN AFTER JEREMIAH
PREACHED TO ME IN A DREAM

Nowhere are we safe.
Surely not in love,
Morning ripe at three
Or in the Holy Trinity.

(My God, look after me.)

Where does Grace abide,
Whole, whole in surety?
Or does sin abide
Where virtue tries, in shame, to hide?

(My God, have I no pride?)

Shall I try the whole,
Crippled in my will,
Spatter where it falls
My carnal-fire waterfalls?

(My angel, in compassion, calls.)

Secret, knotted shame
Rips me like a curse.
Unction in my dust
Gives me final thrust.

(My God, consider dust!)

From "THE CONFESSION STONE"

A Song Cycle Sung by Mary about Jesus

6

Bring me those needles, Martha,
I believe I'll knit Jesus a scarf.
Go on snapping those butterbeans. . . .
What time is it?
Let me see now: knit one. . . .
You say it's twelve o'clock?
Snap enough for Joseph and Lazarus:
They'll be home before you're through.
Martha, what time is it? Purl two. . . .
Purl one,
Knit one,
Purl two. . . .
If I had the star of Bethlehem. . . .
I'd knit three. . . .
. . . and light His sky. . . .
Where was I, Martha?
Oh yes, knit one,
Purl seven. . . .
What time is it, Martha?
Knit three. . . . purl ten. . . .
It can't be near three o'clock.
Where was I? Knit. . . . purl twelve. . . .
Purl nothing. . . .
Martha, don't leave me alone.
Where are you, Martha?
Martha, where are you, Martha?
Martha!

MARGARET DANNER

was at one time assistant editor of *Poetry: A Magazine of Verse,* perhaps the most important publication of its kind in the English-speaking world. She has lived in Chicago most of her life and obtained her education there at Loyola and Roosevelt Universities. In 1945 she won second prize in the Poetry Workshop of the Midwestern Writers' Conference at Northwestern University. Further recognition came with the Harriet Tubman Award, an award from the American Society for African Culture, and a John Hay Whitney Fellowship.

In 1960 Mrs. Danner became the first Poet in Residence at Wayne State University, Detroit. At this time she founded Boone House, a poetry and art center that provided stimulation and working space for aspiring Negro writers and artists. She was one of the American poets who participated in the First World Festival of Negro Arts held in Dakar, Senegal, in 1966. Her work has been published in magazines and anthologies, and she has made a recording of her poems. A booklet, *To Flower: Poems,* was issued in the Counterpoise Series in 1963.

A number of Mrs. Danner's poems give vivid expression to her deep interest in African life and art. Such work has an engaging exoticism balanced and enhanced by ironic perception. Her verse in general is full of color and movement and vibrant imagery, which in some instances must compensate for structural flaws.

I'll walk the tightrope that's been stretched for me,
And though a wrinkled forehead, perplexed why
Will accompany me, I'll delicately
Step along. For if I stop to sigh
At the earth propped stride
Of others, I will fall. I must balance high
Without a parasol to tide
A faltering step, without a net below
Without a balance stick to guide.

THESE BEASTS AND THE BENIN BRONZE

("*Africans are beasts.*" THE REVEREND CARROLL)

Dave Garroway's Mr. J. Fred Muggs often thumps
quite a rhythmical thump with his feet,
doesn't he? Sometimes he seems pretty clever.

But irrespective of his Fauntleroy and other neat
and obviously dear apparel, have you ever
wondered whether he, if his very life

depended on it, could take a stave from a barrel
and curve a small, smooth, round stick? And while
it is evident (from the ever growing strife

resulting from the wider scope of guile)
that a talking snake is working overtime,
not even in the bible did a dragon

horse or serpent use a sculptor's knife,
nor can as sacred a thing as a Hindu cow carve or
even draw one of those lovely Indian girls, or a wagon

for that matter. And I've studied Bushman for years
and can, along with the thousands of others who
loved the big brute, attest to his dignity and near-

human intelligence, but he couldn't have fashioned one
    true

free form or, if given a knife, whittled one whistle.
No history has chronicled a four-legged sculptor,

so how can we reconcile this beast epistle
to this pure Benin bronze, for with all
the contraptions that moderns have to aid them
their skill doesn't compete
with these masks, so what beast made them?

Over the warts on the bumpy
half-plastered wall
just recently slapped with peach-
colored calcimine,
Carter the artist curved tan
mahogany chalk African women, tall
and arched with a swaying grace.

He then conjured nine
green palm trees and three Egyptian
perfume urns,
so that those whom some might call
flotsam, pimps, jadies,
after tippling their cheap, heady
drinks, could discern
the palms, waving cool, green, shady,
over the (dancing now) African ladies.

THROUGH THE VARIED PATTERNED LACE

("I salute the divinity in you." GREETING FROM A FELLOW BAHA'I)

As I look into each different face,
I am exalted.
I am exalted to recognize His Grace
shimmering through the varied patterned lace.

There is this Good in every man
whether Russian or French, Italian or American
and glowing so in you,
O, Ibo, Yoruba, Zulu, Congolese, Fan.

I look at you and feel It flooding me.
Divinity must win the race. It will not be halted.
We are all small sons of one clan.
I am exalted.

DUDLEY RANDALL
is both publisher and poet. His Broadside Press has issued a series of beautifully designed broadsides of poems by leading Negro poets. He was born in Washington, D.C., in 1914 and was raised and educated in Detroit, Michigan. He received his B.A. degree from Wayne State University and his M.A. degree in library science from the University of Michigan. He is presently a librarian at the Wayne County Library. During World War II he saw duty in the South Pacific, and in 1966 he visited Russia, meeting some of its outstanding writers. There he added to his knowledge of Russian poetry, his translations of which have appeared in several publications. He has written articles and stories for *Negro Digest* and other periodicals, and has given readings of his poems and lectures on poetry. Two of his ballads have been set to music. His poems appear in *Beyond the Blues, New Negro Poets: U.S.A.*, and other anthologies.

Randall's poems are quiet, reflective, and somewhat formal in structure. His best work shows perceptiveness and good craftsmanship.

BOOKER T. AND W. E. B.*

"It seems to me," said Booker T.,
"It shows a mighty lot of cheek
To study chemistry and Greek
When Mister Charlie needs a hand
To hoe the cotton on his land,
And when Miss Ann looks for a cook,
Why stick your nose inside a book?"

"I don't agree," said W.E.B.,
"If I should have the drive to seek
Knowledge of chemistry or Greek,
I'll do it. Charles and Miss can look
Another place for hand or cook.
Some men rejoice in skill of hand,
And some in cultivating land,
But there are others who maintain
The right to cultivate the brain."

"It seems to me," said Booker T.,
"That all you folks have missed the boat
Who shout about the right to vote,
And spend vain days and sleepless nights
In uproar over civil rights.

* Booker T. Washington (1856–1915) and Dr. William Edward Burg-
hardt Du Bois (1868–1963).

131

Just keep your mouths shut, do not grouse,
But work, and save, and buy a house."

"I don't agree," said W. E. B.,
"For what can property avail
If dignity and justice fail.
Unless you help to make the laws,
They'll steal your house with trumped-up clause.
A rope's as tight, a fire as hot,
No matter how much cash you've got.
Speak soft, and try your little plan,
But as for me, I'll be a man."

"It seems to me," said Booker T.—

"I don't agree,"
Said W. E. B.

When I was a boy desiring the title of man
And toiling to earn it
In the inferno of the foundry knockout,
I watched and admired you working by my side,
As, goggled, with mask on your mouth and shoulders
       bright with sweat,
You mastered the monstrous, lumpish cylinder blocks,
And when they clotted the line and plunged to the floor
With force enough to tear your foot in two,
You calmly stepped aside.

One day when the line broke down and the blocks
       clogged up
Groaning, grinding, and mounted like an ocean wave
And then rushed thundering down like an avalanche,
And we frantically dodged, then placed our heads
       together
To form an arch to lift and stack them,
You gave me your highest accolade:
You said, "You're not afraid of sweat. You're strong as a
      mule."

Now, here, in the hospital,
In a ward where old men wait to die,
You sit, and watch time go by.
You cannot read the books I bring, not even

Those that are only picture books,
As you sit among the senile wrecks,
The psycopaths, the incontinent.

One day when you fell from your chair and stared at the
       air
With the look of fright which sight of death inspires,
I lifted you like a cylinder block, and said,
"Don't be afraid
Of a little fall, for you'll be here
A long time yet, because you're strong as a mule."

my love has left me has gone from me
    and I with no keepsake nothing
    not a glove handkerchief lock of hair picture
    only in memory

the first night the magic snowfall
    the warm blue-walled room we looking at the snow
    listening to music drinking the same cocktail
    she pressing my hand searching my eyes
    the first kiss my hands touching her
    she close to me answering my lips
    waking at morning eyes opening slowly

I approaching her house trembling
    kissing her entering the room
    waking all night writing a poem for her
    thinking of her planning her pleasure
    remembering her least liking and desire
    she cooking for me eating with me
    kissing me with little kisses over the face
    we telling our lives till morning

more to remember better to forget
    she denying me slashing my love
    all pain forgotten if only she comes back to me

◖ MARGARET ABIGAIL WALKER
won recognition with her first book, *For My People,* published as the prize-winning volume in Yale University's Younger Poets competition in 1942. She was born in Birmingham, Alabama, in 1915, the daughter of a Methodist minister, and her early education was received in denominational schools. She was graduated from Northwestern University in 1935 and later took graduate courses under the poet Paul Engle at Iowa State University, which gave her an M.A. degree in 1944. She taught English at Livingstone College and at West Virginia State College before joining the faculty of Jackson State College in Mississippi. She is married and has four children. She has been a Rosenwald Fellow, and she was given a Houghton Mifflin Fellowship for her novel, *Jubilee,* which appeared in 1966.

In his foreword to *For My People* the poet Stephen

Vincent Benét wrote: ". . . out of deep feeling, Miss Walker has made living and passionate speech." The aptness of this observation is borne out by "For My People," "We Have Been Believers," and other poems with related themes. In these the poet depends less upon subtle implications than upon clear, direct statements given poetic force by intensity of language and conviction. There are poems, however, in which the very urgency of her racial awareness overrides their effectiveness as art. Negro history and folklore, legendary heroes like "Bad Man Stagolee" and John Henry have provided Miss Walker with the subjects for vigorous ballads in the folk idiom. Her personal lyrics form a relatively small segment of her total work, but they have substance and should not be overlooked in any attempt at a proper assessment of this poet's achievement.

For my people everywhere singing their slave songs re-
peatedly: their dirges and their ditties and their blues
and jubilees, praying their prayers nightly to an unknown god, bending their knees humbly to an unseen
power;

For my people lending their strength to the years, to the
gone years and the now years and the maybe years,
washing ironing cooking scrubbing sewing mending
hoeing plowing digging planting pruning patching
dragging along never gaining never reaping never
knowing and never understanding;

For my playmates in the clay and dust and sand of Alabama backyards playing baptizing and preaching and
doctor and jail and soldier and school and mama and
cooking and playhouse and concert and store and hair
and Miss Choomby and company;

For the cramped bewildered years we went to school to
learn the reasons why and the answers to and the people who and the places where and the days when, in
memory of the bitter hours when we discovered we
were black and poor and small and different and nobody cared and nobody wondered and nobody understood;

For the boys and girls who grew in spite of these things
to be man and woman, to laugh and dance and sing
and play and drink their wine and religion and success, to marry their playmates and bear children and
then die of consumption and anemia and lynching;

For my people thronging 47th Street in Chicago and
Lenox Avenue in New York and Rampart Street in
New Orleans, lost disinherited dispossessed and happy
people filling the cabarets and taverns and other
people's pockets needing bread and shoes and milk
and land and money and something—something all
our own;

For my people walking blindly spreading joy, losing time
being lazy, sleeping when hungry, shouting when
burdened, drinking when hopeless, tied and shackled
and tangled among ourselves by the unseen creatures
who tower over us omnisciently and laugh;

For my people blundering and groping and floundering
in the dark of churches and schools and clubs and
societies, associations and councils and committees
and conventions, distressed and disturbed and de-
ceived and devoured by money-hungry glory-craving
leeches, preyed on by facile force of state and fad and
novelty, by false prophet and holy believer;

For my people standing staring trying to fashion a better
way from confusion, from hypocrisy and misunder-
standing, trying to fashion a world that will hold all
the people, all the faces, all the adams and eves and
their countless generations;

Let a new earth rise. Let another world be born. Let a bloody peace be written in the sky. Let a second generation full of courage issue forth; let a people loving freedom come to growth. Let a beauty full of healing and a strength of final clenching be the pulsing in our spirits and our blood. Let the martial songs be written, let the dirges disappear. Let a race of men now rise and take control.

My grandmothers were strong.
They followed plows and bent to toil.
They moved through fields sowing seed.
They touched earth and grain grew.
They were full of sturdiness and singing.
My grandmothers were strong.

My grandmothers are full of memories
Smelling of soap and onions and wet clay
With veins rolling roughly over quick hands
They have many clean words to say.
My grandmothers were strong.
Why am I not as they?

Old Molly Means was a hag and a witch;
Chile of the devil, the dark, and sitch.
Her heavy hair hung thick in ropes
And her blazing eyes was black as pitch.
Imp at three and wench at 'leben
She counted her husbands to the number seben.
   O Molly, Molly, Molly Means
    There goes the ghost of Molly Means.

Some say she was born with a veil on her face
So she could look through unnatchal space
Through the future and through the past
And charm a body or an evil place
And every man could well despise
The evil look in her coal black eyes.
   Old Molly, Molly, Molly Means
    Dark is the ghost of Molly Means.

And when the tale begun to spread
Of evil and of holy dread:
Her black-hand arts and her evil powers
How she cast her spells and called the dead,
The younguns was afraid at night
And the farmers feared their crops would blight.
   Old Molly, Molly, Molly Means
    Cold is the ghost of Molly Means.

Then one dark day she put a spell
On a young gal-bride just come to dwell
In the lane just down from Molly's shack
And when her husband come riding back
His wife was barking like a dog
And on all fours like a common hog.
    O Molly, Molly, Molly Means
    Where is the ghost of Molly Means?

The neighbors come and they went away
And said she'd die before break of day
But her husband held her in his arms
And swore he'd break the wicked charms;
He'd search all up and down the land
And turn the spell on Molly's hand.
    O Molly, Molly, Molly Means
    Sharp is the ghost of Molly Means.

So he rode all day and he rode all night
And at the dawn he come in sight
Of a man who said he could move the spell
And cause the awful thing to dwell
On Molly Means, to bark and bleed
Till she died at the hands of her evil deed.
    Old Molly, Molly, Molly Means
    This is the ghost of Molly Means.

Sometimes at night through the shadowy trees
She rides along on a winter breeze.
You can hear her holler and whine and cry.
Her voice is thin and her moan is high,
And her cackling laugh or her barking cold
Bring terror to the young and old.
    O Molly, Molly, Molly Means
    Lean is the ghost of Molly Means.

I talked to a farmer one day in Iowa.
We looked out far over acres of wheat.
He spoke with pride and yet not boastfully;
he had no need to fumble for his words.
He knew his land and there was love for home
within the soft serene eyes of his son.
His ugly house was clean against the storm;
there was no hunger deep within the heart
nor burning riveted within the bone,
but here they ate a satisfying bread.
Yet in the Middle West where wheat was plentiful;
where grain grew golden under sunny skies
and cattle fattened through the summer heat
I could remember more familiar sights.

When I was a child I knew red miners
dressed raggedly and wearing carbide lamps.
I saw them come down red hills to their camps
dyed with red dust from old Ishkooda mines.
Night after night I met them on the roads,
or on the streets in town I caught their glance;
the swing of dinner buckets in their hands,
and grumbling undermining all their words.

I also lived in low cotton country
where moonlight hovered over ripe haystacks,
or stumps of trees, and croppers' rotting shacks
with famine, terror, flood, and plague near by;
where sentiment and hatred still held sway
and only bitter land was washed away.

SAMUEL ALLEN,
a lawyer, who sometimes publishes under the pseudonym "Paul Vesey," was born in Columbus, Ohio, in 1917. He went to Fisk University and while there had the opportunity to study creative writing under James Weldon Johnson. He continued his education at Harvard, New York University, and at the Sorbonne in Paris. As a poet he was "discovered" by the novelist Richard Wright, who had left America to live in Paris. Wright published some of "Paul Vesey's" poems in the journal *Présence Africaine*. While Allen was in the army in Europe, a limited edition of his poems, *Elfenbein Zähne* (Ivory Tusks), with the text in both German and English, came out in Heidelberg, Germany, in 1956. His verse is included in *Beyond the Blues, American Negro Poetry, New Negro Poets: U.S.A.,* and other publications.

Some of Allen's poems are simple and direct. Others are complex in theme and development and tend to be somewhat abstract and difficult.

Sometimes I feel like I will never stop
Just go forever
Till one fine morning
I'll reach up and grab me a handful of stars
And swing out my long lean leg
And whip three hot strikes burning down the heavens
And look over at God and say
How about that!

When I gaze at the sun
    I walked to the subway booth
    for change for a dime.
and know that this great earth
    Two adolescent girls stood there
    alive with eagerness to know
is but a fragment from it thrown
    all in their new found world
    there was for them to know
in heat and flame a billion years ago,
    they looked at me and brightly asked
    "Are you Arabian?"
that then this world was lifeless
    I smiled and cautiously
    —for one grows cautious—
    shook my head.
as, a billion hence,
    "Egyptian?"
it shall again be,
    Again I smiled and shook my head
    and walked away.
what moment is it that I am betrayed,
    I've gone but seven paces now
oppressed, cast down,
    and from behind comes swift the sneer

or warm with love or triumph?
   "Or Nigger?"

   A moment, please
What is it that to fury I am roused?
   for still it takes a moment
What meaning for me
   and now
in this homeless clan
   I'll turn
the dupe of space
   and smile
the toy of time?
   and nod my head.

GWENDOLYN BROOKS
won the Pulitzer Prize for poetry in 1950 with *Annie Allen*. She is one of America's most admired poets. Born in Topeka, Kansas, in 1917, she grew up in Chicago and was educated there—so it is not surprising that much of her poetry is intimately bound up with the life of Chicago's South Side Negro community. Her first collection, *A Street in Bronzeville* (1945), is flavored with the honey and the gall of that life, as are *Annie Allen* and *The Bean Eaters* (1960). She has received an award from the American Academy of Arts and Letters and two Guggenheim Fellowships. In private life she is Mrs. Henry Blakely and has a son and a daughter. Her *Selected Poems* was published in 1963.

The poetry of Gwendolyn Brooks is richly textured, with a distinctly individual tone, sharply defined images, and compelling rhythms. The incisive word, phrase, or line, the penetrating insight into a personality, a place, or an event endow her poems with the quality of surprise and can bring the shock of recognition. There are times when her work seems "mannered," but even on these occasions her originality shines through. Miss Brooks employs traditional forms like the sonnet and the ballad in unconventional ways. Inevitably considered by some as a "spokesman" for her race, Miss Brooks has had valuable things to say, but she has said them as a poet, not as a polemicist.

My Father, it is surely a blue place
And straight. Right. Regular. Where I shall find
No need for scholarly nonchalance or looks
A little to the left or guards upon the
Heart to halt love that runs without crookedness
Along its crooked corridors. My Father,
It is a planned place surely. Out of coils,
Unscrewed, released, no more to be marvelous,
I shall walk straightly through most proper halls
Proper myself, princess of properness.

NEGRO HERO

(*To suggest Dorie Miller*)

I had to kick their law into their teeth in order to save
    them.
However I have heard that sometimes you have to deal
Devilishly with drowning men in order to swim them to
    shore.
Or they will haul themselves and you to the trash and the
    fish beneath.
(When I think of this, I do not worry about a few
Chipped teeth.)

It is good I gave glory, it is good I put gold on their
    name.
Or there would have been spikes in the afterward hands.
But let us speak only of my success and the pictures in the
    Caucasian dailies
As well as the Negro weeklies. For I am a gem.
(They are not concerned that it was hardly The Enemy
    my fight was against
But them.)

It was a tall time. And of course my blood was
Boiling about in my head and straining and howling and
    singing me on.
Of course I was rolled on wheels of my boy itch to get at
    the gun.

152

Of course all the delicate rehearsal shots of my childhood
 massed in mirage before me.
Of course I was child
And my first swallow of the liquor of battle bleeding
 black air dying and demon noise
Made me wild.

It was kinder than that, though, and I showed like a
 banner my kindness.
I loved. And a man will guard when he loves.
Their white-gowned democracy was my fair lady.
With her knife lying cold, straight, in the softness of her
 sweet-flowing sleeve.
But for the sake of the dear smiling mouth and the
 stuttered promise I toyed with my life.
I threw back!—I would not remember
Entirely the knife.

Still—am I good enough to die for them, is my blood
 bright enough to be spilled,
Was my constant back-question—are they clear
On this? Or do I intrude even now?
Am I clean enough to kill for them, do they wish me to
 kill
For them or is my place while death licks his lips and
 strides to them
In the galley still?

(In a southern city a white man said
Indeed, I'd rather be dead;
Indeed, I'd rather be shot in the head
Or ridden to waste on the back of a flood
Than saved by the drop of a black man's blood.)

Naturally, the important thing is, I helped to save them,
    them and a part of their democracy.
Even if I had to kick their law into their teeth in order to
    do that for them.
And I am feeling well and settled in myself because I
    believe it was a good job,
Despite this possible horror: that they might prefer the
Preservation of their law in all its sick dignity and their
    knives
To the continuation of their creed
And their lives.

PIANO AFTER WAR

On a snug evening I shall watch her fingers,
Cleverly ringed, declining to clever pink,
Beg glory from the willing keys. Old hungers
Will break their coffins, rise to eat and thank.
And music, warily, like the golden rose _simile_
That sometimes after sunset warms the west, _metaphor_
Will warm that room, persuasively suffuse
That room and me, rejuvenate a past.
But suddenly, across my climbing fever
Of proud delight—a multiplying cry.
A cry of bitter dead men who will never
Attend a gentle maker of musical joy.
Then my thawed eye will go again to ice. _metaphor - eye to ice_
And stone will shove the softness from my face.
personification

155

For I am rightful fellow of their band.
My best allegiances are to the dead.
I swear to keep the dead upon my mind,
Disdain for all time to be overglad.
Among spring flowers, under summer trees,
By chilling autumn waters, in the frosts
Of supercilious winter—all my days
I'll have as mentors those reproving ghosts.
And at that cry, at that remotest whisper,
I'll stop my casual business. Leave the banquet.
Or leave the ball—reluctant to unclasp her
Who may be fragrant as the flower she wears,
Make gallant bows and dim excuses, then quit
Light for the midnight that is mine and theirs.

BUT CAN SEE BETTER THERE, AND LAUGHING THERE

"pygmies are pygmies still, though percht on Alps"

EDWARD YOUNG

But can see better there, and laughing there
Pity the giants wallowing on the plain.
Giants who bleat and chafe in their small grass,
Seldom to spread the palm; to spit; come clean.

Pygmies expand in cold impossible air,
Cry fie on giantshine, poor glory which
Pounds breast-bone punily, screeches, and has
Reached no Alps: or, knows no Alps to reach.

Lester after the Western

Strong Men, riding horses. In the West
On a range five hundred miles. A Thousand. Reaching
From dawn to sunset. Rested blue to orange.
From hope to crying. Except that Strong Men are
Desert-eyed. Except that Strong Men are
Pasted to stars already. Have their cars
Beneath them. Rentless, too. Too broad of chest
To shrink when the Rough Man hails. Too flailing
To redirect the Challenger, when the challenge
Nicks; slams; buttonholes. Too saddled.

I am not like that. I pay rent, am addled
By illegible landlords, run, if robbers call.

What mannerisms I present, employ,
Are camouflage, and what my mouths remark
To word-wall off that broadness of the dark
Is pitiful.
I am not brave at all.

They eat beans mostly, this old yellow pair.
Dinner is a casual affair.
Plain chipware on a plain and creaking wood,
Tin flatware.

Two who are Mostly Good.
Two who have lived their day,
But keep on putting on their clothes
And putting things away.

And remembering . . .
Remembering, with twinklings and twinges,
As they lean over the beans in their rented back room
    that is full of beads and receipts and dolls and cloths,
    tobacco crumbs, vases and fringes.

MYRON O'HIGGINS
is a native of Chicago, where he was born in 1918. He attended Howard University, studying creative writing under the poet Sterling Brown and winning the Lucy Moten Fellowship for travel and study. He taught English at Howard before entering the Army during World War II, and after his discharge, he was granted a Rosenwald Fellowship. He spent 1947-48 as a special research assistant at Fisk University. Since then he has traveled extensively in Europe and done graduate work at Yale University. His poems have appeared in magazines and in *One Hundred Modern Poems, The Poetry of the Negro, American Negro Poetry,* and other anthologies. He collaborated with Robert Hayden on a booklet of poems, *The Lion and the Archer,* in 1948.

VATICIDE

(For Mohandas Gandhi)

. . . he is murdered upright in the day
his flesh is opened and displayed. . . .

Into that stricken hour the hunted had gathered.
You spoke. . . . some syllable of terror. *Ram!*
They saw it slip from your teeth and dangle, ablaze
Like a diamond on your mouth.
In that perilous place you fell—extinguished.
The instrument, guilt. The act was love.

Now they have taken your death to their rooms
And here in this far city a false Spring
Founders in the ruins of your quiet flesh
And deep in your marvelous wounds
The sun burns down
And the seas return to their imagined homes.

⫷ M. CARL HOLMAN,
who was born in Minter City, Mississippi, in 1919, has had
his work published in many magazines and anthologies.
While a graduate student at The University of Chicago in
1939, he was awarded the university's John Billings Fiske
Poetry Prize. He also received a Rosenwald Fellowship. For
a number of years he taught English at Clark College, Atlanta, and in addition to his professorial duties edited *The
Atlanta Inquirer*, a weekly newspaper. At present he is In-
formation Officer with the United States Commission on
Civil Rights.

Holman has not yet published a book, but his poetry is known and admired. Formal in structure, it reveals
good craftsmanship, arresting imagery, and a sophisticated
outlook.

Fade in the sound of summer music,
Picture a hand plunging through her hair,
Next his socked feet and her scuffed dance slippers
Close, as they kiss on the rug-stripped stair.

Catch now the taxi from the station,
Capture her shoulders' sudden sag;
Switch to him silent in the barracks
While the room roars at the corporal's gag.

Let the drums dwindle in the distance,
Pile the green sea above the land;
While she prepares a single breakfast,
Reading the V mail in her hand.

Ride a cold moonbeam to the pillbox,
Sidle the camera to his feet
Sprawled just outside in the gummy grasses,
Swollen like nightmare and not neat.

Now doorbell nudges the lazy morning:
She stills the sweeper for a while,
Twitches her dress, swings the screendoor open,
Cut—with no music—on her smile.

Dressed up in my melancholy
With no place to go,
Sick as sin of inwardness
And sick of being so

I walked out on the avenue,
Eager to give my hand
To any with the health to heal
Or heart to understand.

I had not walked a city block
And met with more than ten
Before I read the testament
Stark behind each grin:

Beneath the hatbrims haunting me,
More faithful than a mirror,
The figuration of my grief,
The image of my error.

In the ribs of an ugly school building
Three rapt faces
Fuse one pure sound in a shaft of April light:
Three girls, choir robes over their arms, in a stairwell
      singing
Compose the irrelevancies of a halting typewriter,
Chalk dust and orange peel,
A French class drilling,
Into a shimmering column of flawed perfection;
Lasting as long
As their fresh, self-wondering voices climb to security;
Outlasting
The childbed death of one,
The alto's divorce,
The disease-raddled face of the third
Whose honey brown skin
Glows now in a nimbus of dust motes,
But will be as estranged
As that faceless and voiceless typist
Who, unknown and unknowing, enters the limpid
      column,
Joins chalk, French verbs, the acrid perfume of oranges,
To mark the periphery
Of what shall be saved from calendars and decay.

Taught early that his mother's skin was the sign of error,
He dressed and spoke the perfect part of honor;
Won scholarships, attended the best schools,
Disclaimed kinship with jazz and spirituals;
Chose prudent, raceless views for each situation,
Or when he could not cleanly skirt dissension,
Faced up to the dilemma, firmly seized
Whatever ground was Anglo-Saxonized.

In diet, too, his practice was exemplary:
Of pork in its profane forms he was wary;
Expert in vintage wines, sauces and salads,
His palate shrank from cornbread, yams and collards.

He was as careful whom he chose to kiss:
His bride had somewhere lost her Jewishness,
But kept her blue eyes; an Episcopalian
Prelate proclaimed them matched chameleon.
Choosing the right addresses, here, abroad,
They shunned those places where they might be barred;
Even less anxious to be asked to dine
Where hosts catered to kosher accent or exotic skin.

And so he climbed, unclogged by ethnic weights,
An airborne plant, flourishing without roots.
Not one false note was struck—until he died:
His subtly grieving widow could have flayed
The obit writers, ringing crude changes on a clumsy
          phrase:
"One of the most distinguished members of his race."

JAMES A. EMANUEL,
born in Nebraska in 1921, teaches English at The City College of New York. He has been a cowboy, and during World War II he served in the Philippines. He earned his Ph.D. degree from Columbia University in 1962 with a dissertation on the short stories of Langston Hughes. His poems have appeared in magazines and newspapers and in Langston Hughes's anthology, *New Negro Poets: U.S.A.* He lives with his wife and son in Mount Vernon, New York.

In tight pants, tight skirts,
stretched or squeezed,
youth hurts.
Crammed in, bursting out,
Flesh will sing
And hide its doubt
In nervous hips, hopping glance,
Usurping rouge,
Provoking stance.

Put off, or put on,
Youth hurts. And then
It's gone.

Together, we looked down
When the young horns blared.
We saw glassed-in grins,
Flippant ribbons,
Tough tin cans,
The bridal pair.

We looked down
The corridor of the years
And saw the wreckage,
Tough little monuments
To the Paradise that seldom was.
(Yet our fingers lightly touched.)

The Two looked up.
As if from Eden
They waved. Our hands remembered.
And the tough, young horns
Blared flippantly
Farewell.

Never saw him.
Never can.
Hypothetical,
Haunting man:

Eyes a-saucer,
Yessir boss-sir,
Dice a-clicking,
Razor flicking.

The-ness froze him
In a dance.
A-ness never
Had a chance.

MARI EVANS

is both a musician and a poet. She lives at present in Indian-
apolis, Indiana, where she is associate editor of an industrial
magazine. She is the mother of two sons. She has studied
fashion design and is the composer of several songs.

Her poems, often perceptive, sometimes whimsical,
usually spare and light of touch, have been included in
Beyond the Blues, American Negro Poetry, and *New Negro
Poets: U.S.A.*

There is no beauty
to the world I see
save moments stopped in
Time
preserved
in
unreality . . .
Blood from the streets
from the dim bayou
surges
and the river of it
clouds
my view till hate
with an incandescent **hue**
purges
what was love
burns me
free
. . . of you
There are no birds
no sky
no sea and
only hate
stares back
at me
Where . . .
is the music
I would feel . . .
I hear no song.
. . . just my **hate**
is real . . .

If there be sorrow
let it be
for things undone . . .
undreamed
   unrealized
      unattained
to these add one:
Love withheld . . .
. . . restrained

. . . AND THE OLD WOMEN GATHERED

(*The Gospel Singers*)

and the old women gathered
and sang His praises
standing
resolutely together
like supply sergeants who
have seen
everything
and are still
Regular Army: It
was fierce and
not melodic and
although we ran
the sound of it
stayed in our ears . . .

⊂Ξ NAOMI LONG MADGETT
lives in Detroit and is currently an associate professor of
English at Eastern Michigan University. She was born in
Norfolk, Virginia, the youngest daughter of a Baptist minister. An alumna of Virginia State College, she received her
M.A. degree from Wayne State University. In 1965 she
was awarded The Mott Fellowship in English. Her books
are *Songs to a Phantom Nightingale* (1941), *One and the
Many* (1956), and *Star by Star* (1965).

Mrs. Madgett's poems on racial subjects have a
certain vigor and topical interest, but they are less effective than those in which she develops the enduring themes
of lyric poetry—personal experience, nature, love, and
death.

The This of that and the That of this
And eventually, finally, all-conclusively the This of this
Must be reviewed and dealt with and made sky-blue
        clear.
For birth was but a breath ago
Since the last weary dream
Curled up its edges in its newly-dug
Six hearts of clay forgetfulness.
And since the heat and cold and livingness and black
        decay
Are mint-bright and untold,
And since the burial must be forgot
And the overstatement understated:
The This of that (and unavoidably the This of this)
Must be made plain,
And why and how and what, and sometimes even if.

4

You would not recognize yourself if I should tell you
What truth emerges from your levity and mirth.
Your depth is so disguised that even you
Would be surprised to see your image in the glass
I hold. But let it be;
Enough that I discover you
Over and over, dream and dream again,
In each encounter, and I have a secret
I cannot tell you.

18

Stark day corrodes the silver of the dream
A little, yes.
And caution insulates gloved fingers now
Against enchantment of a certain touch.
But the splendor does not vanish
Because you avert your eyes
Nor the music cease to shiver
Because your words are quick and cold.

I had to tell you.
Turn away if you must; I always knew

That you would have to turn away.

Still I can sing you songs
In silence more eloquent
Than hope or triumph.

G. C. ODEN

wishes to avoid the label "Negro poet." Like Countee Cullen, she is concerned with poetry as an art expressing what is meaningful to everyone, not as a vehicle for protest and special pleading. A graduate of Howard University and its law school, Miss Oden is a resident of Greenwich Village and is a supervising editor with a publishing house. In 1955 she was awarded two John Hay Whitney Fellowships for creative writing. She has had poems in *The Saturday Review, The Poetry Digest, The Half Moon,* and other magazines. She is represented in *American Negro Poetry* and *New Negro Poets: U.S.A.*

Miss Oden's poems appeal primarily to the intellect, which is not to say that emotion is lacking in them but that feeling tends to be subordinated to ideas. She has an eye for the vivid detail, and she combines the literal and the symbolic, the real and the fanciful, in a manner similar to that of Elizabeth Bishop.

THE CAROUSEL

"I turned from side to side, from image to image
to put you down."

LOUISE BOGAN

An empty carousel in a deserted park
rides me round and round,
forth and back,
from end to beginning,
like the tail that drives the dog.

I cannot see:
sight focusses shadow where once
pleased scenery,
and in this whirl of space
only the indefinite is constant.

This is the way of grief:
spinning in the rhythm of memories
that will not let you up
or down,
but keeps you grinding through
a granite air.

The skyline of New York does not excite me
(ferrying towards it) as mountains do in snow-steeped
                hostility to sun.
There is something in the view—spewed up from water
              to pure abandonment in air—
            that snakes my spine with cold
and mouse-tracks over my heart.

Strewn across the meet of wave and wind, it seems
the incompleted play of some helter-skeltering child
               whose hegira (as all
our circles go) has not yet led him back, but will, ripe
            with that ferocious glee which
            can boot these building-blocks
to earth, then heel under.

One gets used to dying living. Growth is an
end to many things—even the rose disposes of summer—
              but still I
wince at being there when the relentless foot kicks down;
           and the tides come roaring over
           to pool within
the unlearned depths of me.

". . . AS WHEN EMOTION TOO FAR EXCEEDS ITS CAUSE"—ELIZABETH BISHOP

2 images - Bird - air
envisioned about the bird
characterizes of the air: inconstancy of the air
lacks stability

You probably could put their names to them.
The birds, I mean.
Though I have often watched their rushing
about the upper air
(deliberate as subway riders
who are not anywhere near
so orderly),
I have never stopped to inquire the name
of that one or another.
Still, I did take time
to observe them in their dips and circles
and jet-propelled ascendancies.

birds represent men
man in love -

It's all in the wings I am told.
That could be said of angels.
I grant it may be true;
undoubtedly is,
since my informants know more
than I. But,
still, I wonder,
and harbor fear that we all are wrong
to think that birds do fly.
What if, one day, upon the ground with us
we found them;
their wings unable to lift them

anywhere except into a deeper stratum
of despair.
Would it all be a matter of wings?
Does flight depend upon such feathered things?

Or is it air? I do not trust the stuff.
Seeing the birds beating about in it,
I want to say, "Take care; and
don't believe in what it seems you do!"
Sometimes I stray across a small one
I should have said it to;
one who for all his modern design
to sweep and arch the atmosphere
had plummeted, instead, to earth
and worms that do not care about horizons.
If I retreat,
too shocked to cast the benediction
of a single leaf,
understand why:
I know the error in invisible support;
in love's celestial venturing
I, too, once trusted air
that plunged me down.
Yes, I!

The map shows me where it is you are. I
am here, where the words NEW YORK run an inch
out to sea, ending where GULF STREAM flows by.

The coastline bristles with place names. The pinch
in printing space has launched them offshore
with the fishbone's fine-tooth spread, to clinch

their urban identity. Much more
noticeable it is in the chain
of hopscotching islands that, loosely, moors

your continent to mine. (Already plain
is its eastward drift, and who could say
what would become of it left free!) Again,

the needle-pine alignment round S/A,
while where it is you are (or often go),
RIO, spills its subtle phonic bouquet

farthest seawards of all. Out there I know
the sounding is some deep 2000 feet,
and the nationalized current tours so

pregnant with resacas. In their flux meets
all the subtlety of God's great nature
and man's terse grief. See, Hero, at your feet

is not that slight tossing dead Leander?

OLIVER PITCHER'S offbeat and sardonic poems have appeared in anthologies and magazines and as a collection in paperback, *Dust of Silence* (1958). He has acted professionally and is interested in writing plays.

Murderers
of Emmet Till
I salute you
and the men
who set the
    murderers
free I salute
you. Twice.

I salute
the brothers
of charity
who let Bessie
Smith bleed to
death. She
had the wrong
blood type.
It wasn't white.

I salute
all self-anointed
    men
who dole out freedoms to other
    men.

I could go on. But won't. I
salute everything, all things
that infect me with this knot
twisted in my subconscious; knot
of automatic distrust, unravelled.
I salute everything, all things
worthy of my confusion, my awe,
my fury, my cursing, which never
looks good in print . . . worthy of
my tears . . . ALL HONORABLE MEN!
I salute you.

You could go on . . . But won't.

Over the eye behind the moon's cloud
over you whose touch to a Stradivari heart shames
the chorale of angels
over Mr. Eros who tramples the sun-roses
and sits amid willow trees
to weep
over the olive wood
over the vibrant reds, blacks, luminous golds of
decay
over the strength of silence and advantages of
unawareness
over the Rosy Eclipse
over the geyser in the toilet bowl
over the cynical comma
over madness itself
the occupational hazard of artists
over the catcher caught in his catcher's mitt
over oil and opal, blood and bone of
the earth
over the iron touch behind pink gloves
over retired civilizations sunken below levels
shimmering in rusty lustre
over myself
I wave the flag *raison d'être.*

TED JOANS,
poet, painter, jazz musician, was for a while one of the
"Beats" of Greenwich Village. Born on a riverboat in Cairo,
Illinois, July 4, 1928, he has led a colorful, free-wheeling
life. In an autobiographical note for *Beyond the Blues*
(London, 1962) he wrote: "Jazz is my religion. . . . I
have traveled to twenty-eight countries and dug the foreign scene and that's for me. . . . I want to be free now.
. . . Free as the white American that is involved in the
arts . . . Man, it's a big drag to have to create under a
false flag. . . . I don't want much, just to be a *free human
being* and treated as such."

Joans satirized the Beat Generation in a book of car-
toons with commentary, *The Hipsters*. His poems have appeared in a variety of anthologies.

If you should see/a man/walking
   down a crowded street/talking aloud/to himself
      don't run/in the opposite direction
         but run toward him/for he is a *poet!*

      You have nothing to fear/from the poet
      but the truth

It is time for the United States to spend money on education so that every American would be hipper, *thus no war!*

It is time for the garbage men to treat garbage cans as they treat their mothers

It is time for the Union of the Soviet Socialist Republics to raise the Iron Curtain and let the world dig 'em

It is time for all museums of art to stop charging admission fees

It is time for the electric chair to give birth to an electric couch thus enabling the entire family to go together

It is time for Madison Avenue to tell the truth and nothing but the truth so help them Mr. Clean

It is time for square jivey leaguers to stop saying 'he's sick, she's sick, they're sick, sick sick sick'

It is time for the Brooklyn bridge to fall on a boat load of DAR fair ladies

It is time for the races of the world to ball and ball and ball and then there will be no reason for war at all

It is time for the Statue of Liberty to be replaced by a Statue of Uncle Tom

It is time for the Post Office to employ only the blind to sort out the mail

It is time for the police headquarters to share their building with young nuns

It is time for Steve Allen to be the next president of the United States, Dizzy Gillespie Sec of State and Kim Novak our Minister of Foreign Affairs

It is time for jazz and more jazz and some more jazz and still some more jazz

It is time for the American Indians to be made multimillionaires

It is time for the keys to be left in the mail box again

It is time for rhinoceroses to roam the streets of Little Rock and spread joy

It is time for a moral revolution in America

It is time for the world to love and Love and LOVE

It is time for everybody to swing (Life don't mean a thing if it don't swing) yes that is right because

It's time it is time to straighten up and fly right tonight

193

⊏⊨ CALVIN C. HERNTON
writes out of an acute awareness of himself as a Negro artist in America. His poems are, in consequence, intensely personal statements of his social convictions. Some of his writing tends to be strident and loosely organized, with an extravagance of abstractions and more or less private symbols, but nonetheless with flashes of power and insight. "I write because I feel I am being outraged by life," he said in the anthology, *Sixes and Sevens* (London, 1962).

Now living in London, Hernton was born in Chattanooga, Tennessee, in 1932. He studied sociology at Talladega College and Fisk University, and he has taught at several Negro schools. His poems are in *Beyond the Blues, Sixes and Sevens,* and *New Negro Poets: U.S.A. The Coming of Chronos to the House of Nightsong* appeared as a pamphlet in 1964. He has published two books of prose.

Young Negro poet
came from 'way down South,
Tennessee, to be exact,
    thought he had some verse,
    thought he could write,
    real well
    as a matter of fact.

Young Negro poet
came from 'way down South
up North,
New York City,
    found that he had no verse,
    couldn't write so well,
    folks back home had lied—
    what a pity, what a pity.

Young Negro poet
came from 'way down South
just to sleep on the cold ground,
Central Park,
to be exact . . .

    Wake up o jack-legged poet!
    Wake up o dark boy from 'way down South!

Wake up out of Central Park, and walk
    through Harlem Street.

Walk down Seventh Avenue, Eight,
Madison, Lenox, and St. Nicholas,
walk all around—
    it's morning in Harlem.

Wake up jack-legged poet!
Wake up dark boy from 'way down South!
Wake up out of Central Park—
wash your face in the fountain water,
take a long stretch,
light up a cigarette butt, and walk defiantly
    through the streets of Harlem Town.

Here is a place that is no place
And here is no place that is a place
A place somewhere beyond the reaches of time
And beyond the reaches of those who in time
Bring flowers and fruit to this place,
Yet here is a definite place
And a definite time, fixed
In a timelessness of precise vantage
From which to view flowers and view fruit
And those who come bearing them.

Those who come by Sunday's habit are weary
And kiss us half-foreign but sympathetic,
Spread and eat noisily to crack the unbearable
Silence of this place:
They do not know that something must always come
From something and that nothing must come always
From nothing, and that nothing is always a thing

To drive us mad.

GERALD WILLIAM BARRAX
has won awards for his poetry, notably the Bishop Carroll Scholarship for Creative Writing and a gold medal from the Catholic Poetry Society of America. He has read his poems in Pittsburgh high schools on the Poets-in-Person series conducted by the International Poetry Forum there, and he is steadily gaining recognition. He was born in Attalla, Alabama, in 1933 but grew up in Pittsburgh, where he attended the School of Pharmacy at Duquesne University for a year before entering the Air Force in 1953. While in the service, he studied at the University of the Philippines, subsequently earning his B.A. degree at Duquesne in 1963. He is now a postal employee, is married, and has three sons. His poems have been published in the periodicals *Four Quarters, Spirit,* and *Poetry.*

Barrax writes with controlled emotional power, breadth of reference, and richness of language and implication.

Tone - sad
a guilty tone
the tones changed

Its sudden dash from the huddled trees
jerked my head up from the trudge of the hill.
The red truck was instantly there
where neither squirrel nor driver existed

for the other. From low angle I saw
the squirrel bound between the wheels
with the perfect timing of death
and bounce from the sudden rubber wall,

spinning in a quiet furry circle.
My "Oh my God" for it, and me,
changed the purpose of my walking
to walk away my Judas eyes.

When I reached the top of the hill
all my damns for death had been said,
and once before the bend I turned
back to face the guilt of trucks.

Irony.
Note of the unexpected.

Swing high, Iscariot,
Alone and unmourned
On your tree on the high dark hill.

Even your own ears
Will not hear
The creak of the swinging rope
Above the crash of thunder.

But the lightning is less merciful;
In its flashes you can see
On a hill higher than yours
Three crosses,
One higher than the others.

But the noose is tight:
The dark thunder-lightning tableau
Films red
And you become immortal.

Where is the star of Bethlehem?
Oh God
Vanguard has eclipsed it!
There is the star of Bethlehem—
dimly between
Sputnik
&
Pioneer

Where are the carols of Christmas?
listen
the earth carols
diminuendo
the heavens
crescendo

These are the carols of Christmas—
"Upon a midnight clear . . .
beep . . . beep . . . beeP
"Silent night, holy night . . .
beep . . . beep . . . beEP
"Christ the savior is born . . .
beep . . . bEEP . . . bEEP
joy to the . . .
bEEP . . . bEEP
joy . . .
BEEP!

She caught a butterfly
and held it closed
            lightly,
in her hand.
She released it
because the sensation made by its
            fluttering
wings was unpleasant.
When the butterfly let itself be caught
            again
she killed it.

shock principle
irony. the expected and the fulfil

You want to integrate me into your anonymity
because it is my right
you think
to be like you.

I want your right to be like yourself.
Integrate me for this reason:
    because I will die with you.

But remember
each day I will look into a mirror
and if you have not taken more than you have given
I will laugh when I see that I am still black.

CONRAD KENT RIVERS was born in Atlantic City, New Jersey, in 1933. He received his B.A. degree from Wilberforce University and later studied at Temple University and The Chicago Teachers College. He served in the army and now teaches in Chicago. He has had poems in many magazines and anthologies. He is the author of two booklets of verse, *Perchance to Dream, Othello* (1959), and *These Black Bodies and This Sun-burnt Face* (1962).

Commenting in *Sixes and Sevens* on his aims and ideals as a poet, Rivers had this to say: "I write about the Negro because I am a Negro, and I am not at peace with myself or my world. I cannot separate my consciousness from the absolute injustice of hate."

THE INVISIBLE MAN — *image*

(For Ellison*)

Image - the negroe —
Symbol - The white - black issue

Your world is unimportant to me,
I am the man people refuse to see.
My voice is the inner impact of
Everything discontented and lonely.

Your name is meaningless to me,
I am black and white with names.
My soul is a cold grey sheet of
Unrewarded dreams—a satirical design.

I am clustered together like bankers,
Lawyers, judges, doctors, merchants.
I am a bio-chemical accident of epidermis. *symbol.*
A phantom in other people's silly minds.

I am too dark for darkness,
And too black and blue for a shadow.
Because you can see my tears
That makes me disgustingly human.

* Ralph Ellison, author of the novel *Invisible Man*

Come to me broken dreams and all
    bring me the glory of fruitless souls,
I shall find a place for them in my gardens.

Weep not for the golden sun of California,
    think not of the fertile soil of Alabama . . .
nor your father's eyes, your mother's body twisted
      by the washing board.

I am the hope of your unborn,
    truly, when there is no more of me . . .
there shall be no more of you. . . .

And the subway gives such refinement
To weary souls, and white collars,
Now that the melodic music of typewriters
    Is but a thought . . .

Now that the floorwalker, the cigar boss,
The commercial tycoon can be laughed at,
Thought about, cursed out, dehumanized,
    Until nine tomorrow morning . . .

My but the subway is marvelous!
We can dream here, build new worlds.
Let the pregnant stand, let the old folks
Hang on for dear life; we cannot become
Human here, this is our paradise lost.

And like the hum from a drum,
The sub moves on . . .
We must dream quick . . .
Our stop is next . . .

But maybe we should
Ride, ride, ride . . .
To the end of the line.

LEROI JONES

has become in a relatively short time the most controversial Negro writer in America. His plays and poems, with their hard-hitting themes, rawness of language, and undeniable originality, have established him as one of the angriest of "The Angry Young Men." He is an advocate of art as protest and propaganda, and he favors the cultivation of a "black" art which would reject white aesthetic values.

Jones is from Newark, New Jersey, where he was born in 1934. He was educated at Howard University, Columbia University, and The New School for Social Research. While in the Air Force he traveled extensively in Puerto Rico, Europe, Africa, and the Middle East. He has edited magazines such as *Kulchur* and *Yugen* and had his poetry and prose in *The Nation, The Negro Digest, The Evergreen Review,* and other journals. He has written many articles on jazz as well as a book about it, *Blues Peo-*

ple (1963). Several plays, among them *The Dutchman* and *The Slave* have been produced off Broadway. He has published two collections of his verse, *Preface to a Twenty Volume Suicide Note* (1961) and *The Dead Lecturer* (1964). A novel, *The System of Dante's Hell,* appeared in 1966.

Much of Jones's poetry is in no legitimate sense racist or propagandist. He has written personal lyrics and poems dealing with abstract ideas, with jazz, with various aspects of the American social scene. At once free and controlled, they exemplify the subjects and techniques favored by the "nonacademic" poets. His poems can be quite obscure at times, their meaning difficult to grasp. As the leading "Poet of the Negro Revolution," Jones attacks both "Whitey" and "Uncle Tom" with equal vehemence, but the result is more often angry abuse than it is impassioned poetry.

It's such a static reference; looking
out the window all the time! the eyes' limits . . .
On good days, the sun.

& what you see. (here in New York)
Walls and buildings; or in the hidden gardens
of opulent Queens: profusion, endless stretches of leisure.

It's like being chained to some dead actress;
& she keeps trying to tell you something horribly
        maudlin.

e.g. ("the leaves are flat & motionless.")

What I know of the mind
seems to end here;
just outside my face.

I wish some weird looking animal
would come along.

Lately, I've become accustomed to the way
The ground opens up and envelops me
Each time I go out to walk the dog.
Or the broad edged silly music the wind
Makes when I run for a bus—

Things have come to that.

And now, each night I count the stars,
And each night I get the same number.
And when they will not come to be counted
I count the holes they leave.

Nobody sings anymore.

And then last night, I tiptoed up
To my daughter's room and heard her
Talking to someone, and when I opened
The door, there was no one there . . .
Only she on her knees,
Peeking into her own clasped hands.

That force is lost
which shaped me, spent
in its image, battered, an old brown thing
swept off the streets
where it sucked its
gentle living.
                    And what is meat
to do, that is driven to its end
by words? The frailest gestures
grown like skirts around breathing.
                                        We take
unholy risks to prove
we are what we cannot be. For instance,

I am not even crazy.

AUDUBON, DRAFTED

(For Linda)

It does not happen. That love, removes
itself. (I am leaving, Goodbye!
                              Removes
itself, as rain, hard iron rain
comes down, then stops. All those
eyes opened for morning, close with
what few hours given them. With tears,
or at a stone wall, shadows drag down.

I am what I think I am. You are what
I think you are. The world is the
one thing, that will not move. It is
made of stone, round, and very ugly.

BOB KAUFMAN

is identified with the "Beat" poets of San Francisco. He has
had poems in magazines produced by that group, and his
"Second April" and "Abomunist Manifesto" were issued
as broadsides by City Lights Books, famous (notorious, in
the view of some) for the publication of Allan Ginsberg's
long poem, *Howl*. Kaufman's *Solitudes Crowded with
Loneliness* came out in 1965.

Kaufman's poems range in form from the surreal-
istic prose poem to the free-verse lyric. Like other Beat poets, he is a caustic critic of American culture.

On ochre walls in ice-formed caves shaggy Neanderthals
      marked their place in time.
On germinal trees in equatorial stands embryonic giants
      carved beginnings.
On Tasmanian flatlands mud-clothed first men hacked
      rock, still soft.
On Melanesian mountain peaks barked heads were
      reared in pride and beauty.
On steamy Java's cooling lava stooped humans raised
      stones to altar height.
On newborn China's plain mythless sons of Han
      acquired peaked gods with teak faces.
On holy India's sacred soil future gods carved
      worshipped reflections.
On Coptic Ethiopia's pimple rock pyramid builders
      tore volcanoes from earth.
On death-loving Egypt's godly sands living sacrifices
      carved naked power.
On Sumeria's cliffs speechless artists gouged messages
      to men yet uncreated.
On glorious Assyria's earthen dens art priests chipped
      figures of awe and hidden dimensions.
On splendored Peru's gold-stained body filigreed
      temples were torn from severed hands.
On perfect Greece's bloody sites marble stirred
      under hands of men.

On degenerate Rome's trembling sod imitators sculpted
    lies into beauty.
On slave Europe's prostrate form chained souls shaped
    free men.
On wild America's green torso original men painted
    glacial languages.
On cold Arctica's snowy surface leathery men raised
    totems in frozen air.
On this shore, you are all men, before, forever,
    eternally free in all things.
On this shore, we shall raise our monuments of stones,
        of wood, of mud, of color, of labor, of belief, of
            being,
        of life, of love, of self, of man expressed
        in self-determined compliance, or willful revolt,
        secure in this avowed truth, that no man is our
            master,
        nor can any ever be, at any time in time to come.

PERHAPS

Should I sing a requiem, as the trap closes?
Perhaps it is more fitting to shout nonsense.

Should I run to the streets, screaming lovesongs?
Perhaps it is more consistent to honk obscenities.

Should I chew my fingernails down to my wrist?
Perhaps it is better to blow eternal jazz.

Maybe I will fold the wind into neat squares.

A Spanish sculptor named Cherino
Has seen the wind.
He says it is shaped like a coil of hardened copper
And spirals into itself and out again,
That it is very heavy
And can break your toe if it falls on your foot.
Be careful when you are moving the wind,
It can put you in the hospital!

RESPONSE

(For Eileen)

Sleep, little one, sleep for me,
Sleep the deep sleep of love.
You are loved, awake or dreaming,
You are loved.

Dancing winds will sing for you,
Ancient gods will pray for you,
A poor lost poet will love you,
As stars appear
In the dark
Skies.

JULIA FIELDS

was born in Bessemer, Alabama, in 1938. She attended Knoxville College and later taught English in a Birmingham high school. She now lives in New York City. Her poems have been published in *Negro Digest* and in the anthologies *Beyond the Blues, American Negro Poetry,* and *New Negro Poets: U.S.A.*

Late that mad Monday evening
I made mermaids come from the sea
As the block sky sat
Upon the waves
And night came
Creeping up to me

    (I tell you I made mermaids
    Come from the sea)

The green waves lulled and rolled
As I sat by the locust tree
And the bright glare of the neon world
Sent gas-words bursting free—
Their spewed splendor fell on the billows
And gaudy it grew to me
As I sat up upon the shore
And made mermaids come from the sea.

DAVID HENDERSON, now in his early twenties, has begun to receive serious attention as a poet. His poems have been published in *New Negro Poets: U.S.A.* and in the magazines *Umbra*, *7th Street Quarterly*, and *The Black American*. He is associated with the "nonacademic" poets of New York's "East Village" and is a native New Yorker. He studied at the New School for Social Research.

It was Tiny's habit
To go down to the GREAT WHITE WAY
Without understanding the subway ride.

   2
The man asked Bubba to sign
A petition for more fallout shelters.
All Bubba wanted to know was
Which way the bomb was coming—
From Washington Heights
Or Sutton Place.

   3
The boy arrived from Mississippi
And got a room on Seventh Avenue the same day.
Right away he wrote to Mama:
     "Dear Ma,
           I got up here safely.
     I got me a room in Harlem
     and everything is all right."

   4
Black small boy asking Mama
Why the sun shines at night
And she answering that it
Ain't shining at all.
"That's a moon."

JULIUS LESTER
has written articles on music for magazines, composed and published a number of songs, and recorded an album for Vanguard Records. He is, among other things, a folk singer, and has performed in cafés and concert halls. He was born in 1939 in Nashville, Tennessee, where he studied music and literature at Fisk University. He has traveled in the Deep South collecting folk material, and now works with the Student Nonviolent Coordinating Committee. Lester lives with his wife and daughter in New York City.

The following poems, published for the first time, are close in spirit, if not always in form, to the three-line Japanese haiku, for which Julius Lester seems to have a particular affinity.

I

With its fog-shroud the
Bridge looks like the Gate to Heaven.
The water is deep.

II

As we got
Closer, the
Rainbow disappeared.

III

Around the church—
A barbed-wire fence.

IV

The man who tried to
Kill himself Saturday—
I saw him tonight.

V

Spring dawn:
Turning toward the storm cloud,
I lost sight of the bird.

VI

She should be
Here now—
To see the rain.

CARL WENDELL HINES, JR., born in Wilson, North Carolina, in 1940, is a "discovery" of Arna Bontemps, who thinks Hines has written "some of the most authentic jazz poetry of the period." Hines is a gifted musician who has never formally studied music. He played with his own jazz combo while a student in science education at Tennessee Agricultural and Industrial State University, from which he was graduated in 1962. His poems have been published in the anthologies *American Negro Poetry* and *Poets of Today.*

#
yeah here am i
am standing
at the crest of a tallest
hill with a trumpet
in my hand & dark
glasses
on.
    bearded & bereted i proudly stand!
       but there are no eyes to see me.
    i send down cool sounds!
       but there are no ears to hear me.
    my lips they quiver in aether-emptiness!
       there are no hearts to love me.
surely though through night's grey fog mist
of delusion & dream
& the rivers of tears that flow
like gelatin soul-juice
some apathetic bearer of
paranoidic peyote visions (or some
other source of inspiration) shall
    hear the song i play. shall
    see the beard & beret. shall
    become inflamed beyond all hope
with emotion's everlasting fire
& join me

in
   eternal
      Peace.
& but yet well
who knows?

  #
there he stands. see?
like a black Ancient Mariner his
wrinkled old face so
full of the wearies of living is
turned downward with
closed eyes. his frayed-collar
faded-blue old shirt turns
dark with sweat & the old
necktie undone drops
loosely about the worn
old jacket see? just
barely holding his
sagging stomach in. yeah.
his run-down shoes have
paper in them & his
rough unshaven face shows
pain
in each wrinkle.

but there he stands. in
self-brought solitude head
still down eyes
still closed ears
perked & trained upon
the bass line for
across his chest lies an old

alto saxophone—
supported from his neck by
a wire coat hanger.

gently he lifts it now
to parted lips. see? to
tell all the world that
he is a Black Man. that
he was sent here to preach
the Black Gospel of Jazz.

now preaching it with words of
screaming notes & chords he
is no longer a man. no not even
a Black Man. but (yeah!)
a Bird!—
one that gathers his wings & flies
    high
        high
            higher
until he flies away! or
comes back to find himself
a Black Man
again.

⊂ᄅ D. L. GRAHAM
was born in Gary, Indiana, in 1944 and is presently a senior
at Fisk University. The poem reprinted here is from *Black
Song* (1966), a pamphlet of poems with a foreword by the
novelist John O. Killens. Graham works nights, attends
classes by day, and is completing a novel.

coltrane must understand how
i feel when i hear
some un-sunned-be-bopp-jazz-man
try

to find the cause of a man's hurt

soul aint nice it's daddy's backache
the blues my mother felt when she
bore me
in a rat-infested-harlem u.s.a.

its . . .
mammas love and daddys hate—
doing it my way
survival motion set to music